Praise for The Re.

"The Real Fountain of Youth is loaded with information to help you manage your stress!"

~ Dean Shrock, Ph.D., author of Doctor's Orders:
Go Fishing and Why Love Heals

"Kimberly has synthesized a comprehensive approach to not only managing, but also defeating stress. Unfortunately, many suffer and have very little idea where or whom to turn for help. In her book, The Real Fountain of Youth, the reader is given concrete and proven methods for determining the cause and developing healthy and practical solutions that work. I applaud her for the depth of knowledge and wealth of resources shared and am confident anyone reading this book will come away with a solid plan of attack in the battle against stress."

~ Mitchel Schwindt, M.D.

"Kimberly Palm's book is an amazing reference guide for healthy and conscious living. Her research reflects her in depth journey into personal and planetary healing approaches. Beautifully written and formatted for all types of seekers and advanced practitioners, her book is a must "travel companion" for all those seeking holistic healing and inner peace".

~ Kenji Kumara, Quantum Lightweaving®

"I can only describe "The Real Fountain of Youth" as a landmark work in the area of Stress Management. It is easily the most comprehensive book of its kind, addressing the physical, mental, emotional and spiritual aspects of Stress. Even though I have been a practicing Hypnotherapist for more than 40 years and deal with Stress Management in my practice there was much here that I did not know. Both the layman and therapist will find this a valuable resource."

~ Bruce E. Kaloski, Ph.D., Clinical Hypnotherapist
and author of The Case for Reincarnation

"Brilliantly Comprehensive, a Must Read!"
If you are human, live on planet earth you are stressed, guaranteed! The only question is... Do you have a plan to manage that stress or not? Kimberly Palm has not only done a comprehensive job in covering all the causes and types of stress we may have, but has given us a brilliantly comprehensive guide with tools for managing that stress before it makes us ill or even kills us. If you are suffering with any health challenge it is likely to be stress related. The Real Fountain of Youth gives you the tools necessary to change your life and claim your right to live healthy and pain free."

~ Krystalya Marie'
Best Selling Co-Author with Deepak Chopra & Wayne Dyer
Author of the One-Minute Energy Tune-Up series of books and products.

"Whether you are looking to identify the sources of stress in your life or understand its nature, or if you desire new approaches to stress reduction, this book will help. Congratulations to Kimberly Palm for creating this helpful and well organized guide through the 21st century epidemic of stress induced dis-ease."

~ Dr. Julie Glass, ND

"From the very essence of love, Kimberly Palm gifts Humanity a most important, transformative treasure with The Real Fountain of Youth. Never judgmental or preachy, and in a language both easy to read and rich with multidimensional wisdom, Ms. Palm expertly crafts what is the most pervasive global health issue of our times as if she personally sits with the reader, her bedside manner purely empathetic and impeccable. Sifting through the cultural blinders and misinformation about stress, with ease she brings to the surface the true causes of stress and also allows the reader to make up their own mind. And with grace she offers the solutions. Most rare indeed is a work devoted to a healthcare, medical, bio-psychological subject so truly rooted in the heart, wherefrom all healing is born."

~ Pietro de la Luna, Healer and author of the Yeshu'a series

"Highly recommended to everyone. It would be great, to see this book, as a mandatory read for our kids in the school systems. Then we are teaching them priceless information that will help their life now & forever to come."

~ Kristi Vaughan, D.C.
Holistic Doctor of Chiropractor, Irvine California

"Positively Empowering! As a nurse, my medical profession and personal Near-Death Experience account, have led me to be more determined than ever to increase my knowledge of the Afterlife. As I continue my research into all areas of this phenomenon, I feel a sense of responsibility to share with others information that I personally feel has the potential to be used as powerful tools. Kimberly Palm has managed to do just that! As I read The Real Fountain of Youth, I was so impressed that I couldn't put it down! My reasoning is simple, I feel that many times valuable information is shared but not processed to the magnitude it deserves due to delivery of the message. In my opinion, Kimberly has managed to create the needed balance to increase not limit her audience. I feel she accomplished this by clearly demonstrating her professional experience in the medical field coupled with words to paper that won't cause the reader to walk away scratching their heads as they try to comprehend the information given. I strongly encourage those of you interested in *expanding your awareness of how to manage stress once and for all to most definitely add this tool to your 'toolbox'."*

~ Erica McKenzie, B.S.N., R.N., author of Dying to Fit In

"Kimberly Palm's new book is an insightful look into how stress invades every aspect of our life, mixing critical research on stress with personal experience. I highly recommend this to anyone who wants to better understand how stress is effecting their life and how to break free from its causal relationship to illness and depression in each of our lives."

~ Edward Phillips, BSHSA, MBA,
Founder/CEO Naturopathic Economics

"As a Registered Dietitian Nutritionist I appreciate the comprehensive information about how toxins in our environment increase stress. Kimberly has put together solid, reliable information backed by research. This is a must read for anyone that is 'sick and tired of being sick and tired' - you probably are carrying more stress than you realize!"

~ Susie Garcia, RDN, #1 International Best Selling Author,
Motivational Speaker, Award Winning Dietitian

"Kimberly Palm has written a book that deals with a topic that affects the majority of the world (Stress effects on health issues). It is not your typical presentation of a subject but an interactive format book that actually becomes a practical tool for the reader to obtain benefits from its use. It is quite a refreshing and intuitive work that delivers results!"

~Fred Valdes, M.D.

"Anyone and everyone who struggles from any level of stress in their lives needs to read this book!
Kimberly Palm has eloquently shared the practices, tools and techniques that healed her stress related illnesses allowing for her own personal

transformation and growth. This book brilliantly discusses the primary causes of stress while providing practical solutions and methods that work. I know because I too have experienced many stress related illnesses and have successfully used most of the tools that Kimberly is recommending in this book. They are real and they work. Kimberly provides a clear roadmap for healing anyone challenged with stress or stress-related diseases. You will find that by understanding the causes of stress and then learning these techniques and taking responsibility as Kim did, you will become your own best healer. If you are ready to heal your mind, body and soul from stress, I highly recommend this book!"

~ Marla Williams - Founder & CEO of Practical Solutions Providing Peace, Purpose and Prosperity

"Kimberly Palm has created a detailed and actionable plan to reduce stress and enjoy some fun at the same time! From my personal favorites chocolate, laughter, and sex this book might surprise you with some very interesting ways to stay young and vibrantly healthy. There are far more stressful situations today than ever before. Kimberly provides the many suggestions and cures. Everyone needs to read this book to live a healthy productive life well into our golden years. Can I hear an AMEN?"

~ Jennifer Elizabeth Masters, Love, Passion and Relationship Coach and author of "Orgasm for Life"

"A must read for those who want to dig deeper than skin deep and get to the root of premature aging and disease. Stress! The author expertly explains the many kinds of stress we face and provides practical tools on how to manage them so the reader can live a happier, healthier, lovefilled life."

~ Jane Pitte, Founder and CEO of Sheer Miracle Minimalist mineral makeup and organic skincare handmade weekly by real humans.

"In 'The REAL Fountain of Youth', Kimberly Palm uses an interesting blend of eastern and western medicine, philosophy, science and remedies to help us understand her personal journey to "Conquering Stress". Her mission is to share her vast knowledge and experience to help you, and the rest of the world, conquer stress, too."

~ Tony Sidio, Entrepreneurial Coach,
Certified Master Life Coach and Speaker
Two Time Best-Selling co-author of Transform – Your Life, Business &
Health and Against the Grain

THE REAL FOUNTAIN
OF YOUTH

An Introduction to
the P.E.A.C.E. Stress Management
System®

KIMBERLY PALM

Spiritual Growth Journeys, LLC
2021

Important caution

This publication contains the opinions and ideas of the author and is sold with the understanding that neither the author or the publisher are engaged in rendering medical, health, psychological, or any other kind of personal or professional services in the book. Nor is anything in this book intended to be a diagnosis, prescription or cure for any specific kind of medical or psychological or emotional problems. If the reader requires medical, health, or other assistance or advice, a competent professional should be consulted.

The author and publisher specifically disclaim all responsibility for any liability, loss or risk, personal or otherwise, that is incurred as a consequence, directly or indirectly, of the use and application of the contents of this book.

DEDICATION

This book is dedicated to the Great "I Am" Creator

And

*To Dr. Masaru Emoto, because water is life
and Dr. Emoto taught us how to heal the water*

CONTENTS

ACKNOWLEDGEMENTS

My thanks and gratitude to all the people I have learned from and who have inspired me over the years, supported and helped me to create this book. A great big hug and thanks to my friend and book editor Victoria Leo, who was an amazing support to me through this process. I am grateful for all of my amazing friends, both local and on social media, who have supported me emotionally with their encouragement and cheerleading and have also given me feedback about the concepts in this book.

A special thanks to Sarah Nash - without your friendship, honesty, feedback, love, support and encouragement, this book would never have been possible. Thanks to the late Dr. Wayne Dyer and thanks to Bruce Lipton, PhD for all of your teaching work on this planet. A special thanks to Louise Hay whose books, CDs and programs not only transformed my life but helped me get to the point in my life where I could share this with the world. Last but most important, thanks to my creator Mother/Father God and Yeshua Christ who asked me to write this book, as well as my guardian angels and guides who helped me through every moment of its creation.

INTRODUCTION

For thousands of years humans have searched for the "The Fountain of Youth." Spanish explorer Juan Ponce De León died while trying to find the "Fountain" in Florida. Kings, political leaders, philosophers, scientists, religious people and other people from all walks of life have worked hard to invent or find The Fountain of Youth. No one has found it or invented it yet. While none of us know what tomorrow may bring, a magic youth pill or elixir of immortality is an unlikely part of our immediate future. I do believe, however, that there is something we all have access to RIGHT NOW that can fulfill some of the promises of the fabled Fountain. Are you ready to learn what this thing is and how you can use it to live a longer, happier and healthier life? I thought so! Let's start with some basics.

According to cellular biologist Bruce H. Lipton, PhD (author of The Biology of Belief, 2008), 98% of illness and disease is caused by stress that we create and 2% of illness is inherited through DNA or epigenetics. So, only 2% of cancer cases are inherited through DNA. The American Medical Association (AMA) has reported that between 80 and 85% of all illnesses are caused by, or made worse by, stress. The Centers for Disease Control and Prevention (CDCP) states that 90% of doctor visits are for stress-related disorders. The International Agency for Research on Cancer and the World Health Organization have concluded that 80% of cancers are due to lifestyle, not genetics, and this is a conservative number. I recently spent some time interviewing my own personal doctors, including a few M.D.'s, a few N.D.'s and a few

Chiropractors and every one of them agreed that 100% of their patients were suffering from stress-related illness.

There are hundreds of medical studies that are convincing on the role of stress in illness and disease. Can physicians or therapists help you with stress? Doctors are not taught about how to deal with stress in medical school and most mental health therapists do not have specific training in the area of stress. A study done in 2012 by the American Psychological Association (APA) said that 50% of all physicians and other medical practitioners [nurses, medical assistants, mental health practitioners and etc.] suffer from burnout and many of those quit. Another study done by the American Stress Institute involved a survey sent out to physicians all over the U.S. which came back showing that 90% of American physicians are stressed out. I have been coaching physicians and mental health therapists in the area of stress for 5 years at the writing of this book, so I know this is a major problem.

It seems clear that, until medical science discovers the fabled Fountain of Youth, we need to focus on what we have here and now, which is stress management. There is currently no magic pill, food, or liquid that will give you long life, perfect health and make you look like you did when you were 20. However, if you learn how to manage all the areas of stress in your life, you may live longer, healthier and happier.

Since various types of stress also cause rapid aging of your cells and skin, you may also retain a more youthful look by managing stress. I also believe that if we want to save future generations from inheriting cancers and other illnesses through cellular stress passed down through the DNA, we should be teaching stress management to our children, both at home and in the schools. This way we have a chance of decreasing the amount of cellular stress that future generations will inherit through epigenetics, from our children's stress. As you read this book, you will discover all the different types of stress, what stress does to your body, and you will learn how to start managing your stress to change your life and health.

Why You Need This Book (and how I developed the P.E.A.C.E. Stress Management System®)

My life has been devoted to seeking and learning truth, wisdom and knowledge, and sharing what I learn with others. I have used my journey and experiences to create a business to teach people skills that will help them to heal their body, mind and spirit. I started off my life with a strong connection to God. When I was only five years old, I picked up my mother's Bible and read it from cover to cover. As a teenager, I began studying metaphysics because I wanted to understand the meaning of life and death. I was eager to learn the truth about everything, including why I existed and where I was going after death. Over 35 years ago, I was misdiagnosed by a physician, which could have had deadly consequences. Luckily, I listened to my inner voice or intuition that knew something was wrong with the doctor's information. I began searching for information to find the proper diagnosis and treatment and was able to help myself.

Over the years I had many more wrong medical diagnoses and times when physicians would shake their head and say, "I don't know what is wrong with you". There was no diagnosis. In addition to not getting the answers I wanted from my physicians, I had the same experience with mental health counselors. I never learned anything that helped me to manage the anxiety I was experiencing. Each time that I didn't receive the answers I was looking for, I wanted to fix myself. I also wanted to prevent illness and have a happier life, so I studied natural healing, alternative medicine, vitamins, supplements, herbs, essential oils, diet, exercise, nutrition, naturopathic medicine, Ayurvedic medicine, other alternative modalities, energy healing, quantum physics, stress management, meditation, self improvement and spirituality.

All of the research and practice has served me well. Not only have I been able to heal myself repeatedly over the years, but as time went on, people would come to me to find out how to heal their colds, flus and other problems. Also, as a result of all my health research and training in energy work, along with my certification in Level II Usui Reiki, I am now able to use many types of energy healing on myself and my clients. My family was made up of nurses and doctors and even though I didn't become a nurse or doctor myself, I am helping people to heal their body, mind and spirit. Some of the information I have gleaned has also come from working in different aspects of the medical industry for 23 plus years.

When I was in my late 30's and early 40's, adrenal burnout hit me as a result of many years of chronic stress. After 4 years spent repairing my adrenals, I now help other people to do the same. I also learned how to reprogram my brain for happiness and success, which I now teach my clients how to do. In addition to everything I have done to heal myself over the years, I went to some amazing alternative practitioners, including naturopathic doctors, acupuncturists, body talk practitioners, massage therapists, homeopathic doctors, Reiki practitioners and energy healers. The combination of modalities helped me to heal my body, mind and spirit.

Many people forget that healers need to receive healing from others! As a result of their amazing help, I have become a champion for the naturopathic and alternative health industry. I also realize today that integrative medicine, incorporating traditional medicine with alternative medicine, is very important. Every one of us is a unique thumbprint of God and we all need to use different supplements, modalities and ways to heal our body, mind and spirit.

During all of my years of body, mind and spirit research, which I will continue until I leave this world, I have had the opportunity to read hundreds of books. Out of all of those books there has been a handful of people who have inspired me to become the healer and teacher that I am today. Some of these people include: Bruce H. Lipton, Louise Hay, Wayne Dyer, Greg Braden, Amit Goswami, Gay Hendriks, Thich Nhat Hanh, Ram Dass and Joyce Meyer. I am very grateful to these beautiful souls and the wisdom that they have shared with the world.

After many years of meditating, I was able to further develop my intuitive, empathic and clairaudient abilities that I was born with, for more insight, body and mind connectivity as well as an ability to really hear God's voice. I also gained the ability to communicate with my guides and angels. When I was 43 years old, I heard God's voice, which told me that my purpose on earth was to be a healer and teacher. God told me to go out into the world and use the knowledge I gained to teach and heal people. Off I went, back to college to get certified to teach meditation and mindfulness. I also got certified in Reiki and learned many other types of energy healing. After graduating with my certification to teach meditation and mindfulness, I started a new healing business, in February of 2011. Up until 2011, I had been life and business coaching people since 1996.

When I started my business, I focused on being a meditation instructor, medical intuitive, health coach and life coach. At that same time I had been reading The Biology of Belief by Bruce H. Lipton, PhD. I had already studied stress management, quantum physics and energy healing for many years, so everything he said in his book made sense to me. Dr. Lipton's book was the turning point in my career. As I mentioned earlier on in this introduction, Dr. Lipton states that 98% of illness is caused by stress we create from birth onward (both conscious and subconscious) and the other 2% is inherited through epigenetics.

This confirmed everything I already knew about stress, since my own illnesses have been stress-induced. I also learned about epigenetics and how stress damages DNA and otherwise affects every cell in our body.

In the meantime, I was teaching meditation classes and my students were coming to me after class with all sorts of emotional stress problems and wanting my advice. One day, I was thinking about Bruce Lipton's book and all of the stressed out people I meet every day, and I made the decision to focus most of my business on teaching people how to manage stress. I had spent years studying stress management techniques and using them on myself, as well as creating my own unique tools for managing stress. I am very grateful to Dr. Lipton and his book because it has helped me to fully live my purpose of teaching and healing people.

Think of stress in the form of thousands of pieces in a body mind spirit puzzle. Everyone has emotional stress, but there is also many other types of stress that affect the body, mind, spirit and the energy body too. When I began teaching stress management to people, I decided that in order for my clients to be healthy and happy, they needed to learn how to manage all of the different pieces of that stress puzzle, not just one. There are hundreds of different types of stress, which we will discuss in the first chapter of this book. My program covers all the types of stress. My work includes teaching local seminars and workshops along with teleseminars and webinars.

Since I started my business, I have been receiving what I call "downloads" from God and Yeshua in the early hours of the morning like midnight, 3:00 a.m. and 5:00 a.m., a time when I should be sleeping. One morning I woke up and received information from Yeshua on what I should be doing in my life. He asked me to call my stress management coaching program "The P.E.A.C.E. Stress Management System® and he told me to share this program with everyone on the earth." I asked, "Why P.E.A.C.E."? The answer was, "This program will create peace in the lives of everyone who learns it. The initials represent the 4 major areas of stress, from which all of the types of stress emanate. The P is for physical stress. The E is for emotional stress. The C is for chemical stress and the last E is for environment stress." Then, Yeshua said, "I am the Prince of Peace and this program will bring peace into the lives of anyone who uses it. He asked me to take this program to every corner of the earth, and when I asked him how I should accomplish that task, he told me that I must introduce it in the book that you are reading now.

After I received my entire download, I promised God and Yeshua that I would share this program with everyone who is interested and wants to improve their live. I spent 5 years of my life writing this book and poured 30 plus years of research and life experience into the pages of this book. Now I am sharing this program in this book. My hope is that this book will go to every land and every nation and be printed in every language so that people all over this planet can create happier, healthier lives. I am so very grateful that God entrusted me to share this with you and the rest of the world. I am honored to be the message bearer.
How to Use this book

This book is intended to teach you what stress is, and how and why stress affects you. You will also find guidance that you can use to start making positive changes in your life. This book is not intended to diagnose or treat any mental or physical health problems.

This book is but a sampling of my knowledge, experience, research and the work I have been doing with my clients since 1998. Please use this book as a workbook for making some positive changes in your life. At the end of each chapter, you will find homework assignments that will help you start managing stress in your life.

This book alone cannot solve all of the problems in your life. However, if you use the information wisely and do the Action Items for Managing Stress at the end of each chapter, you may create some positive life and health changes. It is up to you to change your life. No one will wave a magic wand and make it all better for you. We are all on a journey and have to learn our own individual lessons and make good choices in our lives.

My Intention for You

My wish and intention for you who is reading this book right now is that you will live a happier, healthier and longer life.

CHAPTER 1
WHAT, WHY AND HOW OF STRESS

What Is Stress?

There are many definitions of stress, depending on whether it is being defined by a medical researcher, the DSM-5 for mental health or popular book authors. Here's my favorite: "Stress is anything tangible or intangible that is harmful to your body, mind, spirit (energy body), life or relationships." Tangible or intangible means anything from a car accident or fight with your spouse to you smoking cigarettes or eating deep-fried fast foods.

Over the years I have heard many doctors, therapists and other folks say that some stress is good for you. Good stress, in their view, is the type of stress you have when you are taking a test, have a project due or you are running in a race. I am here to tell you that this is NOT the truth. If all stress is harming you in some way, then there is no such thing as good stress. It might seem that excitement, emotional pressure and time constraints force some people to do well at a task, sport event or test but - as you are about to find out in this chapter - your body and brain do not agree with this idea of "good stress." In fact, the time stress and pressure are making you mentally and physically sick. So, how can that possibly be good for you?

During my 15 years of studying stress, I have found that the 4 major types of stress (physical, emotional, chemical & environmental), each have 4 subtypes within them:

Stress that can be completely prevented. Example: maintaining or putting gas in your car so it doesn't break down on the highway.

Stress that can be deleted. Example: choosing to not watch the (always negative) news.

Stress that you can reduce. Example: work-related stress.

Stress that has to be managed but which you cannot delete, prevent or reduce, like an injury or a relative dying. When someone close to you dies, you need tools to deal with the grief or get some counseling so you can heal.

I like to say that stress is a 2,000 piece puzzle. You are probably thinking, "What on earth is she talking about?" Well, there are thousands of different types of stress and if you really want to live longer, healthier and happier, you will need to learn how to reduce, manage, delete and prevent every single one of them.

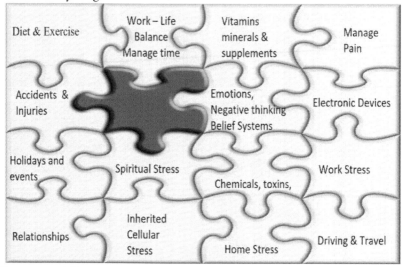

Figure 1.1: The 2,000 Piece Stress Puzzle

Why Stress Is a Worldwide Epidemic

Every year we hear about flu outbreaks, antibiotic resistant illnesses and possible pandemics but stress is ten times more dangerous than all of those things combined. The stress epidemic alone causes more premature death than any disease that has ever been on the planet. I mentioned earlier in this book that between 80% and 98% of illness is caused by stress, according to different sources, and I have had doctors tell me that they believe 100% of their patients are suffering from stress-related illness. The World Health Organization has stated that stress is the "health epidemic of the 21st century" and is estimated to cost American businesses up to $300 billion a year. The fact is that every person on the planet experiences some form of stress every day. Whether it's emotional, dietary, economic, political, environmental, chemical or other, we all are bombarded with stress-causing problems every day.

Are you hoping that doctors or scientists will find a cure for the stress epidemic? It may be a while! Unlike pandemics and epidemics that can be cured or prevented with a vaccine or pill, the stress epidemic will never be cured with a one shot solution. Can you even get help from your doctor? One of America's healthcare secrets is that if you go to see your doctor for stress, they cannot help you. In a study conducted by the American Psychological Association (APA) on doctors across America, 50% of doctors are burned out and stressed out. Minneapolisbased Physician Wellness Services conducted a survey of 2,069 physicians with Cejka Search, a St. Louis, Mo.-based health care executive search firm. Over 87% of respondents said they feel moderately to severely stressed or burned out daily. The question is, how can we manage stress if there will never be a magic cure and who will help us if our doctors can't?

The good news is that we all have the ability to stop the stress epidemic from killing us. We are all in control of removing this stress epidemic from our planet.

> ➢ First, everyone needs to change their perceptions of negative or stressful events. Each person perceives stress differently. The people who have positive perceptions of what happens in their lives are healthier and happier.

➤ Next, we all need to learn how to manage, reduce, prevent and delete stress.

➤ The last thing we all need to do is take responsibility for our problems, commit to making change in our lives and do the work that needs to be done to live healthier and happier. We are in total control of our stress. However, if we all walk around complaining but not doing anything about stress, we will never get any better.

➤ The choice is truly up to you and me. Either we learn to manage stress and live a healthy and happy life, or we continue on the way we've been living and fall victim to the world's most dangerous epidemic.

Throughout history people have suffered with stress, but no one really talked about it or knew what it was. Humans experience 100 times more stress today than we did prior to the 21st century. Thanks to doctors and scientists like Dr. Bruce Lipton (author of The Biology of Belief), we are finally bringing stress into the forefront of our public health discourse and trying to figure out how to tame it.

So, what do you think makes this time in history any different from the last several thousand stressful years? There are several factors that are causing our current stress epidemic that are very different from any period in history:

1. Chemicals in our homes, water, air, environment, food, beverages, clothing, work and other places that did not exist until the industrial revolution and have gotten worse over the last century.

2. Cell phones, T.V.s, notepads, computers and other electronic devices that bombard our bodies, mind and energy field with EMF's and radiation every day.

3. Social media, world-wide news, magazines, newspapers, Internet, TV and other things that give us negative messages and show us negative and violent images.

4. Social pressures on kids and teens, including sex, drugs, and alcohol and the newest one is video game addictions.

5. Societal pressures on women to be skinny, beautiful and have it all. Women are expected to be wives, moms, hold down a job or career and sometimes be caregivers for elderly family members, too. Prior to the women's rights movement, women did not have these types of pressures and rarely worked outside of the home. They certainly were not concerned about being skinny and beautiful while also working as an attorney or owning a business, since basic survival was all-consuming.

6. Mass transportation, motorcycles, planes, trains, subways and most of all car traffic and grid-lock.

7. Political and leadership problems in our own country and all over the world.

8. Socioeconomic problems, like the national debt, as well as the high number of jobless and homeless people in the US.

9. Our sky-high expectations for our life, including our expectations for our behavior and performance.

10. Fast paced social environment where we have to have everything done quickly and everything including our time seems to go at the speed of light. We rush around like lunatics and fuel our speed with coffee and dangerous energy drinks. We want everything NOW, and expect instant solutions to all problems.

11. Overscheduling because we feel like we have to do it all and we believe that we can do it all. I can guarantee that if you compare your to-do list with someone in the 1700's, you will have them beat by 100 to one.

12. Too many choices, opportunities, activities, clubs, sports, careers and other things. Grocery shopping has become difficult because of too many choices. Our ancestors did not have to make this many choices. When you went shopping prior to 1900's, there was one pair of black shoes or one pair of brown shoes. You did not have 500,000 types of shoes to choose from. Psychology research has proven that too many choices leads to stress and decision-paralysis.

There are many more things that I can mention but I don't want to stress you out more listing them all! Here is the key truth: if you want to live longer, happier and healthier you need to learn how to manage all of the major types of stress and hundreds of others that I have identified in my P.E.A.C.E. Stress Management System®. By reading this book you are getting off to a good start to manage Physical Stress, Emotional Stress, Chemical Stress and Environment Stress.

How Do You Deal with Stress? (The Wrong Way and the Right Way)

There is obviously a right way and a wrong way to deal with stress. Unfortunately, many people deal with stress the wrong way, like trying to escape from or run away from stress through the use of drugs, alcohol, sex, food and gambling. Some people become violent and abuse others. Kids and teens deal with stress by fighting, throwing tantrums, acting out, swearing, eating lots of sugary foods, developing eating disorders, arguing, getting bad grades in school, skipping school, doing drugs, running away from home, creating imaginary friends, daydreaming, having sex and much more. Throughout history, men have left their wives and kids because they could not deal with the stress of having a family, including severe financial stress. Some people develop major depression or deal with stress by committing suicide.

If this sounds like you or anyone you know, please do not judge yourself or the people who you know who are going through this. Treat yourself and others with love and compassion. You are a human being and the truth is that parents, schools and universities never taught you how to deal with stress. Since birth, you have not been given the education, tools and training that you need to manage stress, so how can you expect yourself to know how to manage stress? I am here to change that for you. My passion and purpose in life is to help as many people as possible to manage stress and live happier, healthier lives.

There is a right way to manage stress! You can study this book and other books on stress, read up about stress on reputable medical sites on the internet, and work with counselors or coaches like myself who are experts in stress management. This is the effective way to learn the skills you need to manage stress. It's not difficult, but it does take time, patience and perseverance. Just remember, as you contemplate the work you will be doing, that stress management is as close to the Fountain of Youth as you will ever get. So, if you do the work, your payout in the end is priceless.

What are the Symptoms of Stress? How do I know if I am Stressed?
Every person on the earth experiences some type of stress. So if you ask "How do I know if I am experiencing stress?" you're asking the wrong question. The more important question to ask is "How do I know if I am doing a good job of managing stress?" If you are not doing a good job of managing stress, you will know it, because you will have problems with your body, mind, spirit, life and relationships. Some of these are listed below.

Studies clearly show that it's not the actual stress that makes you sick. What harms your body, mind and spirit is the way you perceive and react to stress. These studies aren't wrong, but I believe they are not looking at the entire picture. If we are talking about emotional stress from events that happen, then yes, your perception and reaction to it can have a negative impact on you. However, if we are talking about stress from smoking, using chemicals, eating a bad diet, chronic pain or some of the other types of stress, then the most important thing is to prevent, delete or manage stress. Changing your perceptions and reactions is an important piece, not the whole puzzle.

Here is a list of the some of the most common symptoms or experiences that you can have when stress is impacting your body, mind, spirit or life. Keep in mind that stress is implicated in, or the direct cause of, 98% of illness:

Body Symptoms:	Emotional/Mental Symptoms:	Behavioral Symptoms:
Tired or low energy	Fears	Over-eating
Headaches	Anxiety	Under-eating
Mystery body aches & pain	Restlessness	Angry outbursts
Fibromyalgia	Worrying	Drug or alcohol abuse
Sexual dysfunction	Irritability	Increased smoking
Restless Legs	Depression	Social withdrawal
Chronic Fatigue	Sadness	Crying spells
Over weight	Anger	Relationship conflict
Hormonal Imbalances	Feeling insecure	Poor decisions
Allergies	Lack of focus	Injuring self or others
Heart disease	Burnout	Making too many mistakes
Abnormal blood pressure	Forgetfulness	Poor productivity
Palpitations	Nervousness	Lack of energy
Decreased immunity	Overwhelm	Abusive behavior
Frequent colds and flu	Inability to concentrate	
Digestive problems	Memory problems	
Diabetes		
Hypoglycemia		
Thyroid Disorders		
Autoimmune Disorders		
Sleep problems		

How Your Body Responds to Stress

There are hundreds of ways that all the different types of stress can negatively impact your body. You have already learned that stress causes 98% of illness. When people are emotionally stressed there is an immediate response that you actually can notice, which includes a racing heart, tense muscles, possible sweating, shaking or you may experience other symptoms of an anxiety attack. However, there are many negative ways that your body can react to stress that you may never notice or be aware of, until it's too late.

The first place that stress impacts your body is at the cellular level. Stress causes damage to every cell in your body and if you are eating a bad diet, are emotionally stressed or exposed to chemicals or toxins, you will experience cellular stress (oxidative stress). Environmental stress can reach deep into cells' interiors and alter the genetic material (DNA and RNA) held within their nuclei. This change can be inherited and is referred to as epigenetic stress. When the body becomes too hot, like when you have a high fever, proteins within cells begin to unravel and stop functioning. The proteins of life need to remain at their preferred temperature. If they unravel too much, they tangle up with each other and form a clump that can kill the cell.

The latest cellular research is in the area of telomeres, which are distinctive structures found at the ends of our chromosomes. They consist of the same short DNA sequence repeated over and over again. In humans, the telomere sequence is TTAGGG. This sequence is usually repeated about 3,000 times and can reach up to 15,000 base pairs in length. Telomeres serve three major purposes:

➢ They organize each of our 46 chromosomes in the control center (nucleus) of our cells.

➢ They protect the ends of our chromosomes by forming a cap that is similar to the plastic tip on a shoelace. (If telomeres were not there, our chromosomes might end up sticking to other chromosomes, and then they couldn't function.)

➢ They allow the chromosome to be replicated properly during cell division.

When a cell replicates its nuclear DNA, the chromosomes are shortened. However, because the ends are protected by telomeres, the only part of the chromosome that is lost, is the endmost telomere and the DNA is left undamaged. Without telomeres, important DNA would be lost every time a cell divides - usually 50 to 70 times. This would eventually lead to the loss of entire genes. Oxidative stress shortens the telomeres and is affected by lifestyle, diet, smoking and emotional stress. When the telomere becomes too short, the chromosome reaches a 'critical length' and can no longer be replicated. This 'critical length' triggers the cell to die (apoptosis, also known as programmed cell death). Apoptosis can damage or kill nearby healthy cells by triggering inflammation.

The second way your body reacts to stress – again, without you being conscious of it - is through your adrenals. When you think negative thoughts, perceive a threat or experience pain, your adrenals release the stress hormone cortisol into your body. Adrenals are known as the stress glands and are tiny little glands located on top of both your kidneys. The cortisol released by the adrenals negatively impacts everything from your sleep and your hormones to your immune system, blood sugars, cardiovascular system and more. This is caused the "Fight or Flight" reaction.

God created our bodies to react this way so that we can run away from a Viking or a bear, or lift a heavy object off our loved one. However, when you constantly release this stress hormone, you deplete your adrenals and create havoc in your body. Eventually, the continuous outpouring of cortisol can lead to adrenal insufficiency. Stress can cause cortisol levels in the body to be too high or too low. Taking medications like steroids can also lead to abnormally high amounts of cortisol in your blood and tissues.

If you have chronic stress in your life, chances are that you have some amount of adrenal insufficiency. The best way to find out is to go to your medical practitioner and have your cortisol levels tested. The tests for this are very simple and many insurance plans cover them.

I personally struggled with years of mystery illnesses that I later found out were caused by having adrenal insufficiency. My cortisol levels were completely awry. My doctor told me that it would take anywhere from one to seven years to fix the problem, depending on my ability to follow through with instructions and how much effort I put in. Well, it took me four years to solve my problem but I had struggled with adrenal issues for most of my life, so four years was not much in the scheme of things. I've compiled a list of some of the more common symptoms of an adrenal problem. (There are many more) If you have one or more of these issues, I recommend getting your adrenal function and cortisol levels checked:

➢ Blood pressure too high or too low
➢ Food cravings (salty or sugary)
➢ Weight gain or loss
➢ Allergies or asthma
➢ Feeling tired, low energy or fatigue
➢ Brain fog, fuzzy thinking
➢ problem with focus and concentration
➢ Memory issues
➢ Extreme tiredness after exercising
➢ Dry skin
➢ Inflammation or joint pain
➢ Low blood sugar
➢ Diabetes
➢ Low sex drive (Libido)
➢ Hormone imbalances, severe PMS or bad perimenopause symptoms

> ➢ Dizziness
> ➢ Emotional stress
> ➢ Feeling overwhelmed
> ➢ Short fuse or angry all of the time
> ➢ Anxiety or panic attacks
> ➢ Poor immune system: frequent viruses and infections
> ➢ Inability to sleep 8 hour

How Your Skin, Hair and Nails React to Stress

Have you seen the famous before and after pictures of Presidents of the United States, showing the physical toll of being in the Oval Office? Every president had rapid facial aging. By the time they left office, they looked 10 to 20 years older than when they began their presidency.

Obviously, being president is stressful but every one of us has stress in our lives. What do you think stress has done to your face? What do you think it does to your hair and nails? Research shows that stress can cause premature grey hairs and hair loss, lines and wrinkles, jowls, redness, sagging of the skin and bloating. Some of this is caused by emotional or mental stress and some is caused by cellular stress from chemicals, toxins and poor diet. The double whammy comes when you are emotionally stressed and then you turn to cigarettes, alcohol, drugs or sugary treats to deal with your emotional stress. You probably knew that cigarettes, alcohol and drugs cause your face to wrinkle up, but you might not have known about sugar. We all love to eat cookies, candy, ice cream and other treats but the sugar causes oxidative stress which leads to wrinkled skin.

Basically, your skin is a reflection of the level of stress you have in your life. There is a negative feedback cycle that can happen between stress, skin, hair and nails. People who suffer from skin, hair and nail conditions like eczema, hives, acne, rosacea, psoriasis, alopecia (hair loss) or vitiligo (white spots on the skin) can become emotionally stressed as a result. However, it's also true that being emotionally stressed can trigger these problems or exacerbate them if you already have them. Stress can also lead to more mental health conditions like trichotillomania (hair pulling) and self-mutilation.

There is a new field of study around this problem called Psychodermatology. In 2007, WebMD interviewed Karen Mallin, PsyD, who is an instructor in the departments of psychiatry & behavioral sciences and also dermatology & cutaneous surgery at the University of Miami – Jackson Memorial Hospital. Dr. Mallin stated: "Psychodermatogy is a field that addresses the impact of an individual's emotion as it relates to the skin. I think [psychodermatology] is going to be growing by leaps and bounds [because] dermatology is ready for a more integrated approach with other fields such as psychology, psychiatry and even complementary medicine." An integrated approach to this problem allows for treatments like antidepressants, relaxation therapy, or counseling. Dr. Mallin also told WebMD, "A lot of nerve endings are connected to the skin, which wraps around the organs, so as emotions are played out neurologically, they can be expressed through the skin just as stress can be expressed through gastrointestinal symptoms, increased anxiety, or hypertension."

Remember how cortisol is released into your blood stream when you are stressed? Well, that same stress hormone can increase the skin's oil production, making you prone to pimples. Also scientists now know that a stressful event can trigger autoimmune diseases of the skin and hair like psoriasis, alopecia (hair loss) and vitiligo. Bruce Katz, MD, director of the Juva Skin and Laser Center and the director of the cosmetic surgery and laser clinic at Mount Sinai Medical School, both in New York, explains it this way: "It's the target organ theory, and certain people have different target organs that channel stress," he tells WebMD. "Some people get ulcers, some people get migraines, and other people get rashes as the skin is their target organ."

Your finger nails, just like your skin and hair, are subject to the effects of stress.

Dermatologist Dr. Flor Mayoral, who spoke at the American Academy of Dermatology's SKIN Academy on November 8, 2007, discussed the most common outward signs of stress on your nails. She said that physical or emotional stress, certain diseases, and chemotherapy can cause white horizontal lines to appear across the nails. Other common signs of stress are brittle or peeling nails. Some people develop a nervous habit of biting or picking at their nails when they are stressed.

Other people rub their fingers over their thumb nail which can create a ridge across the nail. This rubbing causes a distortion of the nail plate and, when the nail grows, a raised ridge forms in the middle of the nail. Dr. Mayoral says "Sometimes patients with nail problems are not aware that their habits or tics from being stressed out or nervous are at the root of their problems." As part of her medical practice, Dr. Mayoral gives her patients effective tools for coping with stress. As you read through the chapters in this book you will learn many new skills to manage stress, which will help protect your skin, hair and nails from the effects of stress.

How Your Brain Reacts to Stress

Remember the old TV commercials that warned us "This is your brain on drugs"? Well, I'm going to show you your brain on stress. Since the majority of stress comes to you through your brain, it's important to understand the long term effect that stress has on your brain and what you can do to reverse or prevent these effects. Grey matter in the brain shrinks, memory fails, attention span is shortened, focus, concentration and cognitive ability are impaired and emotions become unbalanced. Anxiety, depression and mental illness are all possible with unrelieved stress. Numerous research studies have been done on the effects of stress on your brain and the results are mind blowing. I couldn't resist the pun!

The gray matter in the prefrontal cortex area of your brain experiences shrinkage due to stress. This part of your brain is responsible for problem-solving, adaptation to challenge, emotional regulation, impulse control, and regulation of glucose and insulin metabolism. A study done at Yale University by Dr. Rajita Sinha and published in the journal Biological Psychiatry showed that people who had major life changes and traumas had greater shrinkage than other people who were less stressed. The stress damaged the mood centers of the brain that regulate pleasure and reward, increasing vulnerability to addiction and decreasing the brain's ability to bounce back.

In another study done by scientists at Yale University, prolonged stress or trauma was associated with decreased volume in areas of the human brain responsible for regulating thoughts and feelings, enhancing self-control and creating new memories. When you are stressed, your amygdala (part of the limbic system of your brain), sends a signal alerting other brain areas that there is a threat. When this happens, your HPA

(HypothalamicPituitary-Adrenal Axis) releases a cascade of hormones including cortisol, the Fight or Flight response you learned about earlier. Long term exposure to this hormone causes your brain volume to shrink. It also interferes with the neurons' ability to send and receive information from other neurons.

When research was conducted on both mice and humans to find out how prolonged stress impacted their ability to think in creative and flexible ways, the scientists found a direct correlation between life events in humans and foot shock in mice with the shrinking of the hippocampus. This is the brain center responsible for forming new, time-sequenced memories. According to another study on two populations with PTSD (Post Traumatic Stress Disorder) - women with childhood sexual abuse and Vietnam vets - their hippocampal volume was decreased by 12 to 26 percent – quite a significant drop! Similar results were found in a study done on people who had recovered from long term depression. There are many more studies being posted every day in medical journals on how stress harms your brain, but I think you get the point.

So if stress shrinks the gray matter in the brain and impairs all of the functions of the brain, what can you do to prevent and reverse this damage? Here are a few things you can do to protect and heal your brain.

> Learn as many tools as you can to manage emotional stress and deal with events and situations that happen in your life. You are never going to be able to avoid things like natural disasters, wars, miscarriage, divorce, job loss and other stressful life events that happen to all of us. However you can learn mental and emotional tools to effectively deal with these things and protect your brain from damage.

➢ Take supplements like EFA's (Essential Fatty Acids) which include things like fish oil, flax oil and evening primrose oil. You can also eat fatty fish like salmon.

➢ Take antioxidants like vitamins A, C and E or eat high-antioxidant containing foods like berries, carrots, citrus fruits, cruciferous veggies (broccoli, Brussels sprouts, cabbage and cauliflower), walnuts and sunflower seeds.

➢ Take vitamin D3. Make sure to take this vitamin with food that contains fat. Vitamin D needs fat in order to be absorbed in your small intestine.

➢ Take plenty of B vitamins which help your brain and your nervous system deal with stress.

➢ Take brain supplements like choline. Good food sources of choline include eggs, soy and brewers yeast.

➢ Eat protein powders (whey, pea, soy) that have lots of amino acids that are important for healthy brain function.

➢ Studies have shown that the following herbs and supplements may be helpful for brain function: Vinpocetene, Acetyl-L-Carnetine, Huperzine A, Bacopa Maneri, Ginko

➢ Biloba, Pyrroloquinoline quinone (PQQ), Phosphatidylcholine, Phosphatidylserine and Alpha GPC. Please check with your doctor before taking these or any new supplements.

➢ Avoid alcohol, nicotine and drugs which harm your brain function. (One alcoholic beverage with a meal, especially red wine, will not harm your brain, but alcohol in excess of 1 glass per day can.)

> ➢ Learn and practice meditation. The latest scientific research shows that practicing meditation daily increases the gray matter in your brain. If stress is shrinking your brain, then meditation is the Anti-Shrinker.

I cannot over-emphasize the importance of a regular meditation habit, to improve your brain, your body and your life. All it takes is 5 to 20 minutes a day to be beneficial. Harvard researchers at Massachusetts General Hospital, demonstrated that meditating had a huge impact in just eight weeks. It altered the brain's gray matter, improved memory, improved sense of self and reduced other effects of stress. Senior author of this study, Dr. Sara Lazar, stated: "Although the practice of meditation is associated with a sense of peacefulness and physical relaxation, practitioners have long claimed that meditation also provides cognitive and psychological benefits that persist throughout the day. This study demonstrates that changes in brain structure may underlie some of these reported improvements and that people are not just feeling better because they are spending time relaxing."

Previous research has shown structural differences between the brains of experienced meditation practitioners and those with no history of meditation, including a thickening of the cerebral cortex in areas associated with attention and emotional integration. In a Harvard study (published in Psychiatry Research – Neuroimaging), 16 people completed an 8 week Mindfulness-Based Stress Reduction (MBSR) program at the University of Massachusetts - Center for Mindfulness. Researchers used MRI's (Magnetic Resonance Imaging) to take pictures of their brains two weeks before and two weeks after the program. The study participants participated in weekly meditation sessions using mindfulness and they also used audio recordings for guided mediation practice. The participants reported how much time they practiced each day. A set of MR brain images was also taken of a control group of non-meditators over a similar time interval. The analysis of MR images also showed increased gray-matter density in the hippocampus, which is associated with learning, memory, self-awareness, compassion and introspection. .

There have been other and very similar studies, including one where neuroscientists at the University of Wisconsin attached 256 sensors to a monk's skull. They discovered that when he meditates, his brain produces a level of gamma waves that is off the charts. He also demonstrated excessive activity in his brain's left prefrontal cortex compared to its right counterpart, meaning he has an abnormally large capacity for happiness and a reduced propensity towards negativity. I won't list every meditation study here; instead, I would like to share my own experience with meditation, particularly mindfulness meditation and guided visualization.

I started learning and practicing meditation many years ago when my doctor recommended it. Meditation transformed my life in such a profound way that I went back to college and got certified to teach meditation. Not only did I heal myself but I also improved my sleep, relationships, memory, focus, concentration, happiness, insight, psychic ability and intuitive ability. I also believe that meditation helped me to heal my physical body. This is why I cannot urge you enough to learn and start practicing meditation. The type of meditation that has the most scientific studies showing positive results is mindfulness (a.k.a. Present Moment Awareness & Insight). TM (Transcendental Meditation) and visualization are also shown to be highly beneficial.

How Stress Impacts Your Career and Finances

Stress has a negative impact on every aspect of your life, including your career and finances. Lack of money creates a stress cycle because stress causes a negative impact on finances. A survey conducted on 3,068 adults, by Harris Poll on behalf of the American Psychological Association (APA) in August 2014 confirmed that financial lack was the biggest cause of stress for Americans.

The main reason that stress has a negative impact on your finances, work or business is because it negatively impacts your decision-making. I mentioned earlier about how stress impacts your brain and especially the cognitive decision-making part of your brain, the prefrontal cortex. If you are a CEO of a company, one stress-driven bad decision can bring down your company. If you are a surgeon, police officer, firefighter, soldier or airline pilot, one stress-induced bad decision can kill people. Other ways that stress affects your job or business include: making mistakes, having accidents and injuries, poor productivity, decreased focus and problems concentrating. Every one of these stress-created problems will keep you from being successful in your life, career and relationships.

If you are in college or studying for board exams, the negative impact on your memory could mean the difference between passing or failing an important test. Of course, when you are stressed, your negative thoughts may be attracting an energy of poverty and financial failure instead of attracting the abundance that you really want. Some people lose their jobs because they cannot handle the stress in their lives.

How Stress Impacts Your Relationships

Every relationship in your life is negatively impacted by stress, including your relationships with friends, family, co-workers, spouses and dating partners. If you are married and/or have children, stress is preventing you from having a healthy relationship with your spouse and kids. The divorce rate in the United States for first time marriages is 50% and it's 75% for 2nd marriages. I believe the reason why divorce is so common now, compared to 100 years ago, is because of the amount of stress we have in our world today.

When you are dealing with stress, it impacts your emotions and personality, causing anger outbursts, depression, rude behavior and other negative things that harm your relationships. If you fight with your spouse in front of your children, it stresses them out too. That is why I insist that both spouses do coaching sessions with me, whenever I coach someone who is married. You need to have both parties focused on stress management or it's not as effective.

When people are married they empathically pick up each other's negative emotional energy. If one person is stressed, then the other person is picking up on those emotions and it negatively impacts them as well. If you teach one person in a relationship how to deal with stress and the other partner does not learn the skills, the untrained partner will continue to react to stress and this puts strain on the marriage. If you are married and reading this book, I cannot urge you enough to share this book with your spouse, or buy them their own copy and read it together. It may save your marriage. During my 28 year marriage, my husband and I have done our best to eat well, exercise, manage stress and constantly communicate our feelings to one another. We get things off our chests and don't go to bed angry.

And sex? How many advertisements have you seen for Viagra and other sexual dysfunction drugs? There are 4 major causes of sexual dysfunction: poor circulation, emotional stress, medications and hormone deficiencies. Three of those four items are all caused by stress and if you are on medications, you are probably taking them because of stress. I believe all sexual dysfunction has stress as a root cause. Remember that 98% of illness is caused by stress?

Whether you are female or male, your sex life will be negatively impacted by stress. I have several past clients who were divorced because they were married to their career, very stressed and tired out at the end of the day. They would come home and their spouse would want sex. But they were too tired and emotionally worn out. Their spouses gave up on them after a while and started extra-marital affairs. Now they are all divorced. A healthy sexual relationship is one of the most important components of a successful marriage. If you do not learn how to manage stress, you cannot expect to have a healthy sex life. The bottom line is that stress not only kills you, it also kills your relationships.

If you have children and/or pets, they are also negatively impacted by YOUR stress. That is because children and pets are very sensitive and pick up all your emotions. If you are constantly having angry outbursts due to stress, it is harmful to the children. Stress will cause you to argue and fight with your kids or create abusive behaviors towards your kids and pets. The result is children behaving badly and rebelling in unhealthy ways. Your pet can react to stress by having accidents or refusing to eat.

If you are tired all of the time because of adrenal problems, chronic fatigue and mental stress, you will not have any energy left to give your children the time and attention they need. I remember when my kids were little and I was suffering with adrenal problems and burnout. It was such a sad time for me because I didn't have the proper energy to give my children. They wanted me to play with them and drive them to the park and other fun places, but I didn't have any energy to do that and of course always felt guilty that I couldn't. If you are a new parent or plan to be a parent someday, I hope you use the info in this book to make sure you have all the energy you need to truly enjoy your children. Time flies by so fast and, before you know it, the kids are grown. I missed out on a lot of my kids' lives, all because my career burned me out and I didn't know how to deal with stress. I hope that this never happens to you.

Of course, your well-meaning parents never taught you how to manage stress when you were growing up, but you are living in a different age. If you teach your kids how to manage stress, you can save them from many years of health, life and relationship problems. Also keep in mind that kids get stressed out, too. They are also impacted by poor diet, lack of exercise, too much video gaming or text messaging, emotional stress, chemicals and all the same things that impact you. Kids get stressed out by peer pressure in school, bullying, mean teachers, difficult homework, divorced parents, death of grandparents and many other things. Make it a point to start working with your children now and teach them simple tools like mindfulness, which is used all over the world to help children cope with stress and do better in school. According to studies, mindfulness can help your kids to focus and concentrate better in school, improve their mood and their memory and heal anxiety and depression.

There is a simple solution to all of the life, money and relationship problems and that is to learn how to manage and prevent stress. Once you do this, you will improve your job or business, your relationships and your finances. As you go through the chapters in this book and apply all of the information you learn and do the homework at the end of each chapter, you will be off to a great start for having a better life.

How Stress Impacts Your Energy Body

According to Quantum Theory, you and everything on the earth, including the earth itself is made of matter, which is just a form of energy. The earth vibrates at a frequency of 528 MHz, the vibration of peace and love. John Lennon recorded his song "Imagine" in 528 MHz for this reason.

You have an energy body that accompanies your physical body. Many religions call this energy body the soul. Middle Eastern and Asian cultures have understood the energy body for thousands of years and have developed practices like Qi-gong, Tai-Chi, acupuncture, Yoga, Ayurveda, meditation and Chakra Balancing to work with the energy body.

Western culture has only recently begun to understand the energy body, how it works and what to do to keep it healthy. Humans who vibrate at a frequency of 500 MHz or more are vibrating at the frequency of Love and are more connected to the energy of creation (God). When you vibrate at this frequency, your energy body is healthy, which also creates health and healing in your brain and physical body. If your body vibrates at frequencies lower than 500 MHz, you have a higher chance of mental, physical and even spiritual illness. Unfortunately, your energy body is subject to stress just like your mind and physical body.

As a result of stress, your vibration can be lowered, your energy can be drained and you can get holes and damage to your energy body. When your energy frequency is lowered, drained or damaged in any way, it creates illness in your mind and physical body. Think about it this way: illness shows up first in the energy body, then it shows up in your mind or physical body. As a result of all the research that has been conducted over the last century into energy and how it impacts the mind and physical body, a whole new health industry has sprung up, called Energy Medicine.

There are many ways to test your energy or energy body to see if there is a problem. Here's a list of some of the more known methods of energy testing:

➤ Thermographic imaging equipment. A non-invasive and radiation-free safe way to scan the entire body. Right now it is commonly used for breast cancer detection.

➤ Energy testing equipment used by some naturopaths and chiropractors. One common machine is called the Rife machine and another is the German BioResonance Machine.

➤ Acupuncture and Chinese Medicine

➤ Muscle testing or Kinesiology

➤ Pendulum Dowsing, which can be done by yourself or by someone else

➤ Ideomotor testing, a self-test using your head and body to test your energy

➤ Chakra testing and balancing

➤ Seeing a medical intuitive or other healer who can see your energy field and/or test your energy using metaphysics. I have been able to see people's energy since I was a child and use that to help my clients.

If stress negatively impacts your energy body, here are some examples of things that harm or drain your energy body and lower your frequency or vibration level:

➤ Negative energy vampires. These are people who are friends, relatives, co-workers, bosses and others who are always grumpy, negative, complaining and bring you down.

➤ Emotional Stress, negative or limiting thoughts and wrong beliefs.

➤ Watching violent sports like boxing or MMA. Sure, you love this stuff, but every time you watch it, you are lowering your vibration. So you need to choose what is more important: a healthy body/mind/spirit or watching violent sports. I know which one I would choose.

➤ Watching violence, horror or crime on T.V. and movies. If you are reading this and you are a huge fan of Game of Thrones or Walking Dead, you may not want to hear this, but it's up to you to choose between energy sucking or energy support. I enjoy a good spy flick or action movie from time to time. However, I only engage in those once in a while and do tons of work on myself to raise and protect my energy level on a daily basis.

➤ Electro Magnetic Frequencies (EMF's) and radiation from cell phones, computers, electronic devices, T.V.'s, disasters like the Fukushima Power Plant meltdown and tsunami and other sources of so-called electro-smog.

➤ Negative speech. Whenever you judge, criticize or say anything negative to or about anyone, you are lowering your vibration.

➤ Arguing and fighting. Every time you argue or fight with someone, your vibration is lowered. Watching others argue and fight also lowers your vibration.

➤ Holding on to grudges or un-forgiveness. Not only does this lower your vibration, but it negatively impacts your heart, breast, lungs and circulatory system.

➤ Eating a bad diet. Some of the many foods that lower your vibration and make you sick include: highly processed foods, fast foods, deep fried foods, hydrogenated fats, foods containing processed white sugars (cookies, candy, ice cream), GMOs, eating gluten when you are gluten intolerant or have celiac disease, soy that is GMO and has not been fermented, foods that contain chemicals and preservatives like MSG and others.

➤ Exposure to chemicals and toxins in your food, soda, water, the external environment, house cleaning chemicals, pesticides, and much more.

➤ Smoking or taking drugs. (My mother died from pancreatic cancer caused by smoking.)

➤ Drinking too much alcohol. A glass of red wine isn't harmful, but drinking too much alcohol makes you sick and depletes your energy.

When you read over the list of things that harm your energy, did you notice that they all have one important thing in common? All of these variables can be prevented or controlled by you! That's right, you are able to control all of these variables, change your lifestyle and do the things necessary to keep your energy body safe and protected. Here is a

THE REAL FOUNTAIN OF YOUTH | 51

list of some of the many things you can do to protect, recharge, raise up, heal and balance your energy body and vibration frequency:

➢ Do your best effort to rid your life of energy vampires. If you can't get rid of them, avoid contact and discussions with them as much as possible and learn protection techniques. Yes, it will be hard to say goodbye to a friend you have known for years, but what is more important to you, your life and health or a friendship with a person who is sucking your energy? The longer you hang out with them, the more you are harming yourself.

➢ Learn how to manage your emotional stress. You can begin by reading the chapter on emotional stress in this book.

➢ Avoid watching violence as much as possible.

➢ Protect yourself and your family from electro-smog and radiation. Purchase devices that you can use to protect your energy. There are many different devices to choose from on the internet. Some of them come in the form of discs you can put on your cell phones, computers and other digital devices. Some are crystals or medallions you wear around your neck or in your pocket. Others are worn on the wrist or plugged into your computer. There are also energy protection devices that plug into your electrical plugs. You will need to research "energy protection" devices on the internet, read the research that has been done on each of them and make a decision which device will work for you and your family.

➢ Utilize energy healing equipment. It is best to see a naturopathic doctor, chiropractor or other expert to try these out for the first time. Once you know how they work, you can purchase your own equipment. Some of the most common are Tachyon Technology, Rife machines and frequency generators.

➢ Watch your speech and try not to say anything negative. Withhold judgement and criticism.

➢ Learn skills for having peaceful happy relationships and/or get counseling if you have people who you do not get along with.

➢ Eat a healthy, anti-inflammatory diet that consists mostly of vegetables and fruits, low fat healthy meats (chicken, turkey and fish), healthy grains and non-meat proteins. (If you eat red meat, make sure it is grass fed.)

➢ Avoid exposure to chemicals and toxins

➢ Do not smoke or take drugs and drink alcohol in moderation

➢ Iodine supplements can be helpful for protecting your body from the effects of radiation. Consult with your doctor because too much iodine is as dangerous as not enough

➢

➢ Learn how to practice energy protection meditations, prayer and/or energy protection exercises. I enjoy teaching energy protection exercises to my coaching clients.

➢ In order to raise your energy vibration and heal yourself, practice giving and receiving love, kindness, compassion and forgiveness to yourself and others. Being of service to others also raises your vibration.

➢ Practice prayer, meditation and/or spirituality. This always raises your vibration.

➤ Practice Tai Chi, Yoga, Meditation and other mind body/energy healing and balancing practices.

➤ Watch uplifting or educational TV. shows, videos and movies

Does that seem like a huge list? Well, there's even more you can do to help yourself!

Watch or listen to comedy. Laughter is the best medicine!

Only hang out with positive, uplifting, supportive and loving people.

Exercise every day. Exercise has a very positive effect on your energy field.

Practice Earthing (grounding). Earthing includes walking barefoot on the grass or sand or sitting with your back up against a tree. You can also use conductive systems that transfer the Earth's electrons from the ground to your body.

According to a study published in 2012 in the Journal of Environmental and Public Health, reconnection with the Earth's electrons has been found to promote physiological changes and subjective reports of well-being, including: better sleep, reduced pain, lowered blood pressure and improved immune system. When you practice this earthing or grounding, you are picking up that healing love energy vibration of Mother Earth. The best part is that all it takes is as little as 15 minutes a day to reap the rewards.

Spend time in nature. The Japanese like to practice Forest Bathing, where you go walking through the forest and take in all the sights, smells, sounds and feelings of the forest. Gardening, walking in a park, hiking, camping and fishing are all great ways to spend time in nature.

Expose yourself to negative ions, which protect and heal your energy field and body, improve your mood and can give you a more positive outlook. Once negative ions reach your bloodstream, the ions are believed to produce biochemical reactions that increase levels of the mood chemical serotonin, helping to alleviate depression, relieve stress, and boost our daytime energy.

The best ways to do this is to spend time by water areas, like the ocean, streams, lakes, rivers and waterfalls. Waves crashing on the beach and waterfalls produce the largest number of negative ions. You can also use Himalayan salt crystal lamps, candle holders or just a bowl of Himalayan salt crystals. If you place a Himalayan Salt Lamp next to your computer it helps protect your body from the effects of the radiation and electro-smog coming from your computer. If you are unable to do any of these things to get negative ion exposure, you can purchase everything from watches to little machines that produce negative ions in your home or on your body.

See certified energy healing and balancing practitioners to receive sessions to heal and balance your energy. There are many different modalities to choose from and you need to try them all out to find out what works best for you and your energy. Every person is different and has different opinions and preferences. I personally have tried tons of different modalities and finally settled with a few that work best for me and make me feel great.

Search on the Internet for information on the following modalities to find out which ones you would like to try out: Reiki, Quantum Touch, Chakra Balancing, Homeopathy, Acupuncture/Acupressure, reflexology, Chi-Gong Energy Healing, magnet therapy, bio-electromagnetic therapy, electrodermal therapy, phototherapy,

Bodytalk, Sound therapy, Aromatherapy, Ayurveda, Biofeedback, Botanical medicine,

Chinese Medicine, Chiropractic, Craniosacral therapies, Shamanic therapy, Creative Art therapies, Healing Touch, Hypnotherapy, Imagery, Indigenous medical practices, Massage and many more.

Take classes and read books on spirituality and religious books to improve your connection to your Higher Power. The more connected you are, the higher your vibration.

Spend time around pets or animals because they vibrate at the frequency of 100% unconditional love.

Use essential oils and Bach Flower Remedies. These oils and flower remedies each have their own special energy vibration that resonates with different mental and physical health ailments and can be used to heal your body, mind and spirit. Some of the ones that I use daily and really like are Valor by Young Living Essential Oils and Frankincense oil, which both vibrate at a very high frequency. If you search online for "Essential Oils for raising your vibration," you will find many of them to try out.

Reprogram your mind for positive thinking, positive beliefs and positive feelings along with reciting positive mantras. You'll find more about this in my chapter on Emotional Stress.

Sound Healing: Use healing music CD's to improve your body, mind and spirit. Sound Healing has been used very successfully in western culture for the last century but has been around for thousands of years. I personally use these whenever I have a health ailment and have seen some very positive results. Three of the leaders in this industry are Jonathan Goldman, Steven Halpern and James Twyman. My favorite healing CD is I Am – Wishes Fulfilled by Dr. Wayne Dyer and James F. Twyman.

Tuning forks and Tibetan Singing Bowls: These both work similarly on your energy body and your mind and physical body. Before using these on your own, do some research and have an expert use them on you first. If you are as sensitive to sound as I am, you can have a bad experience if you are not careful.

Make sure that you regularly cleanse and clear your energy at least once a week. You can learn how to do it yourself, or hire an energy healer like myself to do it for you. All it takes is a few minutes to clear your energy and open you up for receiving the good.

If you want to learn more about your energy body, Quantum Physics, Quantum Entanglement, Quantum Theory, The Energy Field or Energy Medicine, there are many books, papers and studies on these subjects. Some of the many scientists and experts whose work and research I have studied in the field include Albert Einstein, Nicola Tesla, Amit Goswami, Greg Braden, Lynn McTaggart and James Oschman. Research these people and start learning about the Energy Field and how you as an Energy Body relate to the universe and how the universe relates to you. I hope you will be as fascinated and amazed with this field of study as I am.

How Long Will It Take Me to Manage Stress?

The length of time it takes for you to master the art of stress management depends on your learning style and how quickly you can learn and implement the knowledge, and your motivation, determination and willingness for self-improvement, growth and change.

It also depends on the actions you take to put what you learn to good use. Some of us may take a month or two to transform our lives and some of us take years. Remember that the end result is less important than the journey. Any effort you make to achieve peace, happiness and good health is a good thing. The quicker you put what you learn to use, the quicker your results will be because your results are 100% dependent on you. If you read this book and you don't do the activities at the end of each chapter or you don't do anything at all, your life and health will continue on the same as usual. As Doctor Phil says, "How is that working for you?" I really hope you will do the work and start living a happier and healthier life now.

Because this is a workbook, not just a "read about it book," you can expect homework at the end of each chapter, crafted to help you transform your life and health. Let's begin this journey of transformation together.

Reset button exercise: Start paying attention to your body and how it reacts when a stressful event happens. This can be anything from someone fighting with you or yelling at you, to getting fired from your job. Some of the many things you may notice is your heart rate or pulse speeding up, tension in your neck or shoulders, dizziness, butterflies in your stomach, pressure in head, throbbing in temples or anxious feelings. Some people have panic attacks when something stressful happens.

The minute you notice your body reacting to the stress, stop whatever you are doing, place one hand on your belly and another over your heart and take 3 to 5 very long, slow, deep breaths in through your nose and out through your mouth. When you do this breathing, make sure that your belly expands out on your in-breath and your chest rises up. On the out-breath, make sure that your tummy goes in towards your spine and your chest drops. I call this Hitting the Reset Button on your stress, but it's known in the research literature as deep belly breathing. While you do this, notice how your pulse slows down, your tummy relaxes, and pain in your head or tension in your shoulders and neck recedes. Learn to use this technique regularly to help protect your body from reacting to stress.

Before and after comparison: Before beginning Chapter 2 of this book, make a list of all of the health issues and symptoms you currently have. Consult the list of health problems that I listed earlier in the book to make sure you haven't left anything out.

As you use this book and practice what you learn, start paying close attention and notice how your health problems and symptoms change when you are stressed. For example, you might notice fibromyalgia or arthritis pain that gets worse, gaining more weight if you are already overweight, more frequent colds and sinus infections, symptoms of diabetes worsening and other changes. Keep this list somewhere safe.

After you have practiced and used all of the information in this book for 6 months, go back to your list and see how many of those problems you still have. Of the ones you still have, notice how many of them have improved. It takes up to 6 months for major transformational change in your life. This is similar to the before and after pictures you see with

THE REAL FOUNTAIN OF YOUTH | 59

weight loss programs. When I work with my clients I give them a comprehensive assessment where we rate everything in their life and health. They are able to see measurable results by watching the numbers change over time.

Go over the list of symptoms of adrenal problems in this book. If you can check off at least two of those symptoms, consider having your cortisol levels checked. If your levels are not perfect, have your physician put you on a diet and supplement regimen and make sure to learn and use as much stress management as possible from this book and other places to heal your adrenals.

CHAPTER 2
PHYSICAL STRESS

There are many ideas that come to mind from the phrase "physical stress." For purposes of this book, let's define Physical Stress as the response to anything that is harmful to the physical body.

Because we have control over most of our physical stress, we can make lifestyle changes that will delete or reduce most physical stress. In this chapter I will explore some of the many types of physical stress and explain what you can do to delete, reduce and manage the physical stress that you have control over. However, there are a few types of physical stress that you cannot avoid, control, delete, reduce or manage. These are things like accidents and injuries and world pollution. When you are a victim of stress that is beyond your control, like an accident, all you can do is manage the after-effects, work on preventing or managing the emotional stress that results from the injury, and then work on healing your body. This subject alone could fill many books, so this chapter cannot offer ALL of the answers to the problem of physical stress. What it does, is provide you with what you need to start managing your physical stress right now and for the rest of your life. As you read this chapter, make sure to take notes and use your highlighter pen to fully absorb all of the information and refer back to the most important things later.

Causes of Physical Stress

Let's focus on the biggest causes of stress to your body. You may want to highlight each of the items that apply to you so you can compile an action plan for your particular stressors:

➤ Eating a bad diet
➤ Lack of nutrition or starvation (mostly occurs in cases of anorexia, bulimia, or poverty)

- ➢ Smoking, Drinking too much alcohol, or taking drugs
- ➢ Additives and preservatives in foods, beverages and drugs
- ➢ Deficiencies in vitamins, minerals, antioxidants, amino acids and other things important for a healthy body and immune system
- ➢ Lack of exercise, too much exercise, or doing exercise that is wrong or too hard for your body.
- ➢ Over-exertion or lifting too-heavy weight
- ➢ Hiking too many miles
- ➢ Jogging
- ➢ Xtreme adrenaline hobbies (Mountain Climbing, Bungee jumping, Skydiving, Rollercoasters and etc.)
- ➢ Poor sleep or sleep deprivation
- ➢ Accidents and injuries
- ➢ Repetitive strain on the body, from things like sitting hunched over at a computer
- ➢ (lack of proper ergonomics in the work place)
- ➢ Poor posture and misalignments in the spine
- ➢ Eye strain
- ➢ Chronic Pain
- ➢ Inflammation
- ➢ Viruses
- ➢ Chronic Illness and disease
- ➢ Abuse and battery
- ➢ Surgeries
- ➢ Infections
- ➢ Poor dental hygiene
- ➢ Exposure to electronic devices and EMF's: Cell phones, I-pads and computers, bad wiring in the home and more
- ➢ Radiation from sun, cell phone towers, microwaves, flying in an airplane
- ➢ Travel
- ➢ Wearing clothes that are too tight and constricting

➤ Wearing shoes that are too tight, too small or do not have appropriate arch support

➤ Exposure to extreme temperatures that are too hot or too cold. Holding bladder to long

Throughout this chapter I will be covering some of the things on this list in more detail and giving you information on how you can manage stress. If you want to work on items not covered in this book, you will have to do some research or work with a coach or medical practitioner.

Dietary Stress (and why what you put into your mouth is stressing you out)

Every month, doctors, scientists and nutritional experts come out with their version of what diet we should be eating. Of course, they argue over which diet is best. If each one of them thinks their diet is the best, and they have credentials we can trust, who do we believe? After over 27 years of studying the research on diet and nutrition, I have concluded that most disease – including the common arthritis, heart disease and diabetes - is caused by inflammation. I have also discovered that the foods that create inflammation in the body are the same ones that cause obesity, diabetes, heart disease, high blood pressure and other diseases. Stress also causes inflammation in the body, so you will understand when I say that the best diet is an anti-inflammatory diet.

There are entire books devoted to anti-inflammatory diets and some of them are even good. Let's focus on the most important points:

First of all, you need to make sure that you are eating plenty of fruits, vegetables and fiber containing foods.

Second, the 3 biggest foods that cause inflammation in the body are sugar, bad fats and processed foods. If you can decrease your intake of sugar, you will decrease your inflammation. Not only does sugar cause inflammation, but it also lowers your immune system, feeds cancer cells and makes them grow. Sugar also raises your triglyceride levels, leading to diabetes, heart disease and high blood pressure. High Fructose Corn Syrup is one of the worst types of sugar and has been shown to cause obesity, diabetes and metabolic syndrome.

Processed, bleached white sugar is the 2nd worst of all types of sugars. This is the kind of sugar found in many cookies, candies, cakes, pies, and more. Breads, pasta, grains and other carbohydrates turn into sugar in your body, but are not as bad as eating a candy bar. Whole grains are much healthier for you, but they are still carbohydrates and also turn into sugar. It is beneficial for you to limit the amount of carbohydrates you eat and try to stick with complex healthy carbohydrates like whole grain breads and cereals, instead of white processed flour products. It is also beneficial to cut out candies, cakes, cookies, pies and all those other bad sugars.

I am first to admit that I enjoy my chocolates once in a while, so I will not tell you that you have to stop eating candy bars for the rest of your life. However, the rest of my diet is very clean and anti-inflammatory; in my case, "once in a while" is very rarely.

I also take tons of anti-inflammatory supplements and manage my stress, so I don't worry about it. If you take care of yourself in every way, you can eat some occasional candy. [Not if you're diabetic, of course!]

Over the years many doctors have recommended low fat or non-fat diets. While decreasing your fat intake is good, we still need fats for our brain to function properly. The nerve fibers inside and outside the brain and spinal cord are wrapped with many layers of tissue composed of a fat (lipoprotein) called myelin. This myelin sheath is like insulation around electrical wire. When this myelin sheath is damaged, as in multiple sclerosis (MS), nerves do not conduct electrical impulses properly. Fat is necessary for the myelin sheathes so if you don't have enough fat in your diet, your myelin will be damaged, causing neurological problems.

The goal is to decrease your intake of harmful or bad fats while getting adequate amounts of healthy fat to support your brain and body. Fat is also needed for energy, muscle tissue and much more. The fats that cause the most inflammation are hydrogenated fats, so you want to avoid them. There are healthy fats you should be eating every day that will not cause inflammation and are important for your body. The best kind of fats are the polyunsaturated fats found in nuts, seeds, avocados and fatty fish. They contain omega 3 and omega 6 which can lower bad cholesterol (LDL – low-density lipoprotein) and raise your good (HDL – high density lipoprotein) cholesterol. When using oils, the healthiest oils you should be eating every day are extra virgin olive oil, avocado oil and extra virgin coconut oil.

Another type of fat that can cause inflammation is the fat associated with red meats like beef, lamb, mutton and pork. Some doctors say that it's beneficial to cut down on the amount of red meat that you eat. However, there is a bit of a loophole! Studies are now showing that grass fed organic meat is healthier for you and creates less inflammation than traditional feedlot-raised animals. My family and I love hamburgers, steak and roast, so whenever I prepare it, I purchase grass fed, organic animals. We also like to eat pork once in a while and when we do, we make sure it is also organic and pasture-raised.

The last item of the three inflammation causing foods I mentioned earlier is "processed foods." The North American diet tends to contain too many processed foods. In Europe (France, Italy and Greece) and Asia, where most foods are prepared fresh daily, there is very little consumption of processed foods. These countries have much lower rates of inflammation and disease than in North America and hence longer life spans.

The reason processed foods cause inflammation, is because they contain lots of chemical additives, artificial flavors and preservatives, processed salt and bad fats. Also, when you process fruits and vegetables, you remove many of the beneficial vitamins and nutrients. If you eat out at restaurants a lot, you will eat a lot of processed foods. If you want to decrease inflammation, it is important to try to prepare as many of your meals as you can at home and prepare them with fresh ingredients. Because of all the food allergies I have had over the years, I have had to prepare most of my food at home. My family rarely eats out at restaurants. When my family and I eat out, we pick restaurants that prepare all of the food fresh from scratch and use fresh organic ingredients. Over the years I have healed almost all of my food allergies, but I still choose to prepare my food at home to avoid all of the bad stuff that is common in restaurant food.

When food is processed and put into a can, jar, package or frozen dinner, it loses some of the important vitamins and nutrients. This is another good reason to prepare your food fresh at home or eat at restaurants that do the same. Most frozen dinners are high in salt, preservatives, chemicals and additives that are not good for the body. There is one exception and that is if you buy organic brands of frozen prepared foods. They are still not as good as freshly prepared food but the organic meals, like the ones made by Amy's, Cascadia Farms and similar brands are worth exploring. They still tend to be higher in salt, but there are also lower salt versions of some meals.

Unlike processed frozen meals, frozen vegetables and fruits are actually better than fresh vegies at the store, because they are picked and then frozen immediately which preserves their full vitamin and nutrient content. When you buy fresh vegetables and fruits in the produce section, they are not always fresh. Between the moment they are picked and when you buy them, they can be sitting for a long time on trucks, in warehouses and then in the store before they make it to your table. Every moment that the fruits and vegetables sit before you eat them, they are losing important vitamins and nutrients. Canned foods lack many of the nutrients that fresh vegetables and fruits have because of the heating process they go through in order to be put in a can. Also many canned foods have the cans lined with BPA's which have been shown to cause cancer. I use use canned foods sparingly, when I am in a hurry or unable to find a fresh vegetable or fruit that I need for a recipe. Canned soups appeal to my kids and may appeal to you. So some may choose to have them once in a while in lieu of a sandwich.

One more thing I would like to share with you about diet and inflammation is the use of supplements to decrease inflammation in the body. Earlier I mentioned that I take special supplements every day to decrease inflammation in my body. Supplements are a great way to reduce inflammation and improve your health. Keep in mind that supplements are not a replacement for an anti-inflammatory diet, but they will help aid you, especially if you cheat and eat a candy bar or burger once in a while. The ones that I take daily and believe are beneficial based on my research, include: flax oil, fish oil, Bromelain, tart cherry, turmeric and resveratrol. Before taking any of these, make sure you check with your doctor first, because some of these tend to have a blood thinning effect, which can harm you if you are on certain medications or have to get surgery.

If you would like to learn more about anti-inflammatory diet, lifestyle and supplements, I recommend the work of Dr. Stephen Sinatra, an integrative cardiologist, bone health and anti-aging specialist. His book Arthritis Interrupted helped me to get rid of all my knee pain. You can find out about Dr. Sinatra and see all of his products and books on his website, www.drsinatra.com.

Chemicals, Additives and Preservatives in Food

Do you remember learning that food colorings like "Red #40" caused hyperactivity in kids? It seems to me that every year of my life since then, there has been more information showing the negative impact of chemicals, additives and preservatives on our bodies. Babies and children tend to be impacted the most by these things, of course. The human body is meant to eat and drink things that come from nature like meats, vegetables, fruits, nuts and grains. When we put things into our body that are made of chemicals or that have been created in a lab of items not from nature, we need to proceed with caution. Scientific studies on many chemicals have shown changes in brain chemistry and harmful effects on the body, including cancers. If you are a highly sensitive person like I am, it's imperative to stay away from chemicals, additives and artificial preservatives in foods.

I have suffered for years with an allergy to MSG (monosodium glutamate), which has made it very difficult to eat out at restaurants, since many of them use MSG in the food. [Glutamate is the molecule that makes meat and cheese taste so savory.] I always laugh at the fact that most of the things I am allergic too are basically dangerous chemicals that kill you or chemicals that make you sick, like MSG. According to www.truthinlabeling.org, MSG is prevalent in over 40 different food ingredients and is added to foods as a flavoring or preservative. MSG is also found in shampoos, conditioners, soaps, cosmetics, drinks, candy and gum. According to General and Systematic Pathology MSG disrupts brain chemicals because of the glutamate, which is an important chemical messenger in your brain. Too much of any particular neurotransmitter can become an excitotoxin- over-excite cells to the point of damage. Too much glutamate in the brain leads to various enzymatic cascades that result in neuron death. This may explain why many symptoms reported from MSG consumption are neurological in nature.

Despite the fact that the FDA and the World Health Organization say that MSG is safe as a food additive, millions of people all over the world still have bad reactions after eating it or using a shampoo or other product that contains one of the 40 types of MSG. Over the years, the FDA has received many anecdotal reports of adverse reactions to foods containing MSG. These reactions, known as "MSG symptom complex", include:

- •Headache
- •Flushing
- •Sweating
- •Facial pressure or tightness
- •Numbness, tingling or burning in the face, neck and other areas
- •Rapid, fluttering heartbeats (heart palpitations)
- •Chest pain
- •Nausea
- •Weakness

Many countries in the world have banned chemicals that are considered safe in the U.S. (www.topinfopost.com). For example, most of the Western world including 98% of Western Europe, does not drink fluoridated water because of its harmful effects on the body and brain. Dentists in the United States tell their patients that fluoride prevents cavities. However, the tooth decay rates in Europe have declined over the past 50 years as they have in the U.S., even without fluoride.

Many countries have banned MSG as well as Olestra, brominated vegetable oil, potassium bromate, azodicarbonamide, BHA, BHT, rBGH, rBST and arsenic, and a feed additive named ractopamine.

Ractopamine is a growth stimulant banned in several countries because lab tests have shown it being extremely harmful to health.

According to an article written by one of my favorite doctors, Dr. Joseph Mercola on www.Mercola.com, more than 3,000 food additives -- preservatives, flavorings, colors and other ingredients - are added to U.S. foods. Many of them have been banned and deemed too harmful for consumption in other countries. Dr. Mercola also stated, "90% of the money Americans spend on food goes toward processed foods loaded with these additives, so it's no wonder most people are carrying a hefty toxic load that can wreak havoc on their health." If you want to see a list of foods banned around the globe but still allowed in the U.S, check out a book called Rich Food, Poor Food, by nutritionist Mira Calton.

If you are going to be a warrior at managing stress and living longer, you need to read all of the labels on the processed foods and beverages in the store. Make sure that the only ingredients are ones that come from nature and are safe for your body. If the product you are buying is organic and it says right on the front of the package "No MSG, additives, artificial colors, artificial flavors, or preservatives," then they are probably okay. Believe it or not there are many products in the supermarkets that say the word natural on the package and they really contain harmful additives. Natural is not a defined term! Organic should be backed up by a certifying agency that you recognize. So be very careful to read the ingredients list.
In case you are wondering what ingredients you should be looking for, there are 45 or 50 of them and you can always look up "harmful food additives" on the web.

A report on the Gaiam Life website, www.life.gaiam.com, listed the top 10 worst food additives:

THE REAL FOUNTAIN OF YOUTH |71

Artificial Colors

Artificial Flavorings

Artificial Sweeteners (Acesulfame-K, Aspartame, Equal®, NutraSweet®, Saccharin, Sweet'n Low®, Sucralose, Splenda® & Sorbitol)

Benzoate Preservatives (BHT, BHA, TBHQ)

Brominated Vegetable Oil (BVO)

High Fructose Corn (HFCS)

MSG (Monosodium Glutamate)

Olestra

Shortening, Hydrogenated and Partially Hydrogenated Oils (Palm, Soybean and others)

Sodium Nitrite and Sodium Nitrate

Part of loving and taking care of your body and taking care of your family, includes being 100% responsible and accountable for what you put in your mouth and what you feed your family. If you spend time to do the research at reputable websites, you can find out what is good for your body and what is bad, avoid doctor and hospital bills, avoid wasted time, and hopefully live a longer and healthier life. The internet is a plethora of information, so sit down, get educated and start clicking your way to good health.

Vitamins, Minerals and Supplements for Better Health

Are you vitamin and mineral deficient? Having a vitamin or mineral deficiency is very stressful to the body and can cause a laundry list of problems. If you want to live a longer and healthier life, it's important to have the right amount of vitamins and minerals, neither too little nor too much. If you are deficient in vitamins, minerals or antioxidants of any kind, you can have unusual symptoms, health problems and eventually major disease. For example, I used to have frequent migraines through my childhood and some of my adult life. I tried everything I could to get rid of them, until one day I found out that some migraines can be caused by magnesium deficiency. After about a month of taking magnesium citrate every day, my migraines went away and never came back. A deficiency can also cause problems with your immune system, heart, thyroid, blood, and other processes in your body. Some vitamin and mineral deficiencies can also impact your brain function.

Some causes of vitamin deficiencies includes nutrient-deficient fruits and vegetables from depleted and over-farmed soil, overcooking food, inherited genetic mutations (like MTHFR gene) that keep your body from methylation or absorption, microwaving your food, poor diet, sweating out minerals with over-exercise and fever, hereditary conditions, illness, prescription drugs, lack of sunshine, and certain supplements. Fixing one vitamin imbalance can exacerbate low volumes of other vitamins. That's why a comprehensive, rather than piecemeal approach is best.

You are probably wondering "How do I know if I am deficient?" The best way to find out is to go to a Naturopath, MD or Chiropractor who tests for vitamin deficiencies. Other ways to find out is by researching any symptoms you are experiencing with your health or do muscle testing (kinesiology).

In addition to the well-known vitamins and minerals, you also need to make sure that you take and make plenty of antioxidants. An antioxidant inhibits the oxidation (chemically combining with oxygen) of another molecule. Some antioxidants are produced by your body and some are not and have to be taken as supplements. Antioxidants get depleted with age, and other chemical processes, and by taking certain prescription drugs, like statins. Your body also manufactures antioxidant enzymes in order to control free radical chain reactions that can interfere with important metabolic pathways.

Antioxidants play a significant role in your health, as they can slow down your aging by reducing the number of free radicals.

The four main antioxidants that your body makes are superoxide-dismutase (S.O.D.), catalase, glutathione, and Co-Enzyme Q10; you've probably heard of the last one! These are important for your heart, preventing cancer, anti-aging and other bodily functions.

I don't recommend oral glutathione products. The only way to get glutathione, according to

the reputable studies I have seen, is to get an intravenous injection of it or to take supplements or eat foods that help your body to make more glutathione itself. The glutathione that is put into oral supplements does not absorb well.

One of my favorite supplements for helping your body to make glutathione is NAcetyl Cysteine (N.A.C.). This is a supplement that needs to be prescribed by and monitored by a naturopathic doctor or holistic M.D. because in high doses it can be dangerous, but in the correct dose it's very helpful.

My favorite food for helping your body make glutathione and is also very healthy with no side effects, is asparagus. That's right, you can serve your family up some asparagus for dinner and help them to increase their glutathione levels. Think of it as a green and yummy dose of anti-aging and cancer prevention.

After you pass 40 years of age, you might make less digestive enzymes and hydrochloric acid, which are very important for digesting your food. If you are over 40 or you are any age and having problems with your digestion, please consider seeing a natural medicine doctor to get a recommendation for good digestive enzymes. Stress and the subsequent low self-esteem can impact your digestion. I've had my own experience with years of stress messing up my digestive system. I went on digestive enzymes and they have changed my life. I am now able to eat many foods that I wasn't able to eat before. There are special enzymes for digesting just about everything from gluten, grains, proteins, plants, fats, sugars and carbohydrates to enzymes for digesting gas-causing foods like beans, including tofu, and cauliflower.

Helpful bacteria in your digestive system can also get depleted and need to be replaced with supplements. Having beneficial good bacteria in our intestines is important for preventing and fighting viruses and bacterial infections, preventing cancer, preventing and curing chronic problems like IBS (Irritable Bowel Syndrome) and helping us to maintain a healthy weight. If we are stressed out or we take antibiotics, we decrease the amount of healthy bacteria in our intestines. The antibiotics kill off all bacteria in our body, both good and bad.

When our intestinal bacteria is out of balance, we will be more prone to viruses and infections. Our body will also start producing an overgrowth of candida and bring on yeast infections. Candida also causes allergies to molds, fungus, yeast and other things. Candida overgrowth can cause a plethora of health problems. The candida feeds on sugar, and causes us to crave sugar. Craving sugar causes weight gain, which leads to a whole other list of diseases and health problems.

New York Times best-selling author and digestive expert, Brenda Watson, has brought probiotics into the limelight with her PBS special, programs and books about your gut health. Brenda recommends probiotics that slowly release and break down in your small intestine because that is the place where you need the good bacteria. Brenda also recommends taking high quality probiotic supplements that contain at least 10 strains of good bacteria and 15 billion IU's of good bacteria.

There is a belief that eating yogurt is good enough for replacing the good bacteria, but the truth is that any beneficial bacteria that goes into your stomach is destroyed by stomach acid and never makes it down into the intestines where it needs to go, unless you take a coated or special capsule that is meant to only break down in the intestines. I am not telling you to stop eating yogurt because the unsweetened variety does have many health benefits and I personally eat yogurt every day. I am only telling you that if you want your gut to be healthy, you need to take high quality probiotic capsules. My family and I take probiotics every day. Probiotics have cured me from candida overgrowth, allergies to yeast, mold and fungus, cured my IBS and have kept my immune system strong and prevented me from getting colds and infections. Probiotics can also protect your gut when some bacterial infections from food poisoning, drinking bad water and hospital infections like C-Dif. You shouldn't expect probiotics to completely prevent these illnesses! However, if you become ill, you are likely to have a weaker illness than you would without probiotic help and you will recover much faster.

What I have discovered after years of researching and trying out thousands of vitamins and supplements, is that everyone's body is different and reacts differently to supplements based on DNA, genetics and sensitivity. We are all unique thumb prints of God, so you cannot expect to have the same exact results as other people. Just because a study says that something is good for you or helpful for a condition doesn't mean that it is good for your particular body. You could still have a bad reaction or not have the results you expect. Over the years I have had to try out many things on myself until I found the right combination of vitamins and supplements that was beneficial for my body. You have to be adventurous and keep trying things out until you find what works for you, not what works for your neighbors and your mom.

We all need to be wary, because supplements are products being sold by a company that wants to make as much money as possible – period. During my life, I have been sold tons of supplements by people who claimed that these things would give me specific results and then I was extremely let down when I didn't get the results they claimed or I had terrible reactions to the products. Some multilevel marketing sales people run around forcing their products down people's throats and telling everyone that they have to try their product. Some of these people tell stories of how all of their clients have had super amazing results. I will tell these MLM sales people that their product contains an ingredient that I am allergic to and cannot take it. They will then proceed to tell me a lie that their product is good for people with allergies and that none of their clients with allergies react to their amazing product. I have made the mistake of believing these people and taken their product, only to get a bad allergic reaction and have to return the product to the company. I no longer buy any products that contain anything I may be allergic to.

I also research every new product I take and use kinesiology to muscle test the product to see if it will work for me. I highly recommend muscle testing any product before you try it. Most chiropractors or Naturopaths can show you how to do this. Muscle testing works with your energy field because your energy body cannot lie. If the energy says something is bad then you need to honor that. It is also good to get a genetic test done through the two reputable consumer sources (www.23andme.com, National Geographic 2.0) or get specific genetic tests through your medical practitioner and go over the results with a genetic counselor if you want to be sure that the diet and supplements you are putting in your mouth is best for your genetic makeup. Your DNA cannot be changed and cannot lie, so if your DNA says you have a gene mutation that prevents you from methylation of certain vitamins and minerals, you need to do something about this and be careful what you put in your mouth. If your DNA says that you have an inherited allergy to shellfish or some other substance, you have to pay attention and do not take that until you have gone to a Bodytalk practitioner or some other expert who can clear genetically inherited allergies. I personally had tons of allergies cleared by my amazing Bodytalk practitioner. To find out more about what Bodytalk is and how it's beneficial for healing the body and clearing allergies, please go to https://www.bodytalksystem.com/

There are vitamins and supplements you can take for just about every health problem, including stress. It is important, in this stressed-out world we live in, that we take vitamins and supplements to support our bodies and minds. If you have any amount of adrenal problems, you will only be able to heal your adrenals with the help of supplements, healing modalities and stress management. I personally have an arsenal of supplements and vitamins I take daily to help my body and mind deal with stress. I had to try out different supplements until I found out what worked and what didn't. Some of the products that are recommended for stress made me super-hyper, which is the opposite of what I was trying to achieve! So, if you decide to take anything to support your body and mind for stress, proceed with caution and check with your doctor first to find out which supplements are good for you.

Make sure to stop taking something immediately if you have a bad reaction.

Here is a list of some of the vitamins and supplements that have been recommended by doctors. Most of these have been used in either India, Asia or Europe effectively for hundreds of years. Each one of these has different functions for supporting either your brain or your body with stress:

Vitamin C – This one is my favorite because it strengthens your immune system, and is important for every function in your body.
Vitamin D3 ("the sunshine Vitamin;" most people are deficient)
Magnesium
B Complex vitamins – especially B2, B5, B6, B12, Folate
Omega 3's (Found in Fish Oil, Krill Oil, Flax Oil)
Glycine
Chamomile
Valerian
Passionflower
Lavender
Licorice Root (Talk to your doctor, and proceed with caution because licorice root can raise blood pressure and deplete your potassium levels)
Lemon Balm (Melissa)
Rhodiola
Eleuthero
Siberian Ginseng
Panax Ginseng
Ashwaghanda
Lemon Balm (Melissa officianalis)
St. John's Wort
GABA
L-theanine

Phosphatidyl Serine

5-HTP

Relora

Essential oils (You use them in aromatherapy or apply them to your skin mixed with carrier oils - bergamot, lavender, rosemary, clary sage, sandalwood, cedar)

Bach flower remedies (These can be taken in water and also applied to skin)

One word of warning about vitamins and supplements. The vitamin and supplement industry is not completely monitored and regulated like the pharmaceutical industry. There are products on the market that could be dangerous, phony, sourced from toxic areas, contain chemicals and toxins, contain bacteria or have other issues. However, for every bad product, there is also one or more good products. That being said, make sure to research any product before you take it. Make sure that the ingredients have been sourced from a safe and tested supply. Make sure the products are 3rd party tested for purity. Check out the reputation of the company. Read on the internet to see how the products are rated and also see if there are any lawsuits or complaints against the products before you take them. It is also helpful if they have a USP symbol on the bottle or any other government approvals.

Summary

My essential message here is that in order to manage physical stress we all need to pay attention to everything we put into our mouths, including vitamins and supplements. We also need to take supplements to lower inflammation, live longer and be healthier. I can probably fill another book with information on vitamins and supplements, but the most important thing for you to know is that deficiencies stress out your body. You are also stressing out your body if you take doses that are too high or supplements that are wrong for your personal body type. Make sure that you get tested or do research into which vitamins, minerals and antioxidants are beneficial to take daily. I highly recommend doing muscle testing. If possible go get a genetic test to see what is best for you. Always check with your doctor before taking any new supplements, especially if you are on prescription medication.

Move Your Body to Live Longer

How many times in your life have you heard the phrase, "Move it or lose it"? Well, if you don't move it, you will lose your life. According to many studies, sitting all day is equivalent to a death sentence. An article that appeared in the LA Times on January 19th, 2015, cited new research summarizing the findings of 47 studies, concluding that those of us who sit for long hours raise our average risk of cancer, cardiovascular disease, type 2 diabetes and early death. The results also showed that even people who meet daily recommended levels of exercise, have a boost in their likelihood of declining health if they sit for long periods of time. The latest research published in the Annals of Internal Medicine finds that the risk of poor health "is more pronounced at lower levels of physical activity than at higher levels." Those who engage in regular physical activity but still spend a large proportion of their day in sedentary activity were found, on average, to be 30% less likely to die of any cause in a given period than were those who get little to no exercise. But even those who punctuate a long day of sitting with a vigorous workout were estimated to be 16% more likely to die of any cause in a given time than were those who do not sit for so long. Some new studies show that staying healthy is 70% diet and 30% exercise. Exercise has so many benefits including reducing stress, balancing your hormones, improving your sex life, lowering your cholesterol, lowering your blood pressure and all the other benefits that lowered blood pressure and lowered stress bring!

Too little exercise stresses out your body by causing joint problems, problems with your spine and posture, weakening your muscles, ligaments and tendons, taking your hormones out of balance, robbing you of sleep, increasing abdominal fat, increasing your propensity for injuries and osteoporosis, and many other problems. Did you know that even though too little exercise is bad, too much exercise also stresses out your body? If you are someone who runs or bikes many miles, does marathon weight lifting sessions, hot yoga sessions or other types of extreme sports or extreme amounts of exercise, you are creating another score of problems. Over-exercising can cause hormone imbalances, damage to your spine and joints, creating joint pain, the need for future knee replacements and other joint replacements, stress fractures, cortisol and adrenal problems, sleep problems, sexual problems, heart attack and blood pressure problems, propensity for injury and much more. Many runners wind up with knee replacement surgeries and even wind up in a wheel chair before they are old enough for that to be an expectation. Remember all the sages, whose advice points to "Everything in moderation." Any time you do too little or too much of something, it's bad for you. If you do too much of a "good" thing, you will destroy your body.

So you are probably wondering, "How much exercise is just right"? This is kind of like the story of Goldilocks and the Three Bears, because you want the exercise that is just right. Well, according to the results of two 2015 studies published in the JAMA (Journal of the American Medical Association), anyone who is physically capable of activity should try to "reach at least 150 minutes of physical activity per week and have around 20 to 30 minutes of that be vigorous activity," says Klaus Gebel, a senior research fellow at James Cook University in Cairns, Australia, who led the second study. And a larger dose, for those who are so inclined, does not seem to be unsafe, he said. My idea of just right, is at least 20 minutes to 60 minutes of exercise every day of the week and doing a combination of different types of exercise every day. I will explain more about this.

What I have found from coaching clients for many years, is that many people have problems starting an exercise program or quit exercising. Many of the people who quit, do it before they are close to their weight or fitness goal. So right now I would like to talk with you about the many reasons why people either have a problem working out or have a problem sticking with a workout. Here is what I have seen as the major reasons why people have an exercise problem:

Tired all of the time or lack of energy.
Lack of motivation – Self motivation or not having a friend, relative or someone to encourage them.
Lack of knowledge on the importance of exercise or lack of knowledge on how to exercise.

Poor priorities and lack of self-care

Unable to manage time or having wrong perceptions about time. "I don't have time to exercise" is an excuse I hear quite often.

Dropping out from boredom. Doing the same one or two monotonous exercise activities over and over again almost guarantees that you will lose interest.

THE REAL FOUNTAIN OF YOUTH | 83

Taking on an exercise routine that is too difficult for their ability and fitness level and then (predictably) failing at it.

Getting injured or pulling a muscle. Sometime people get stuck in the "Chronic Pain Cycle," which I will explain to you later in this chapter and then they are afraid of going back to exercise for fear of more injury or pain. I have had many people tell me they got hurt while exercising and now they are afraid to exercise again. Sometimes you just have to get back on that horse and start again.

A wrong belief that it will cost a lot of money to do a "good exercise" program. You don't need any money to move your body.

Upper limit barriers – Creating your own blocks to success by making excuses and reasons why you can't exercise or don't have time to exercise. You are the one limiting yourself. No one is telling you can't work out.

I have been coaching people with health, diet and exercise for many years. I have come up with a series of what I call "Easy Exercise Hacks" that I teach my clients and I will share with you now. So without further adieux, here is my list of exercise hacks that you can use to stay healthy and live longer:

To help you stay motivated to exercise, set up a reward system for yourself. Have something fun or important you can work towards like a new swimsuit, a dinner out with your spouse, beers out with the guys, or even a chocolate ice cream cone. You get the picture, just find something you want to dangle as a carrot and put a picture of it on your fridge so you know what you are exercising for. Pick an amount of time it will take for you to earn this item. An example is, after one week of exercising every day, you get a night out with the boys/girls.

Another way to stay motivated is to have a friend or relative to exercise with and hold each other accountable. You can also hire a personal trainer if you want to spend the money. Make sure you get a good recommendation because not all personal trainers are equally skilled.

If you don't have knowledge about exercise, then go do some research and try things out. This is a matter of life or death, so it's worth your time to find out what types of programs and activities you can do for exercise and experience them.

If you are not putting yourself as number one priority by taking care of yourself, you will let down a ton of family, friends and co-workers if you die from stress or health problems related to lack of exercise. You should always be your first priority in life.

Learn time management. This is the first thing I do with all my coaching clients so they have the time to work on improving their lives and health. You can find the time to fit in at least 10 minutes of exercise every day. Studies have shown that even 10 minutes of intense working out each day is good for your health.

Always pick exercise that is beneficial for your fitness level, muscle tone, general physical abilities, balance, strength, flexibility and age. For example if you have never lifted weights before, you don't want to start off lifting 100 pounds or you will injure yourself. You want to start off with two pounds and work your way up as your muscles get stronger.

If you get injured, wait until you recover or your doctor tells you that it's okay to exercise and then start moving again. Do not go back into your full routine like you did before the injury or you will re-injure yourself; instead start off going easy on yourself and work your way back up.

If you don't have money to spend on a health club or other exercise activity, don't worry. Most exercise is free of charge or very low cost like walking, running, bicycling, hiking, playing softball or basketball with friends, doing a workout video from the library, using some exercise bands or weights, swimming, playing catch with your kids and etc.

If you are sitting there and making excuses right now about why you cannot exercise, then you are creating your own limits. (example: "I have small kids" "I work too many hours") I have a question back at you: Do you want to live longer? If you want to live, then stop the excuses and get your butt moving. Sorry, but I have to be straight with you and stand in my truth. If you are having issues with using excuses to limit what you can accomplish in your life, you will need to hire a coach like myself who works on these issues and can help you to remove your limits and blocks to your success.

If you are bored, here is my awesome exercise hack for boredom. Make a list of all of the activities you enjoy doing, like swimming, playing soccer, kayaking, bicycling, yoga, Martial Arts and etc. Then add to the list a few exercises that you don't love but you can live with, for example, interval training or weight lifting. Write up a weekly schedule for yourself and pick a different activity to do every day. When you mix it up, you can never drop out from boredom or lose interest. It's a new thing every day. Now isn't that an easy concept?

Buy a pedometer and put it on your belt, in your purse or pocket. Park your car far away at stores and malls so that you are forced to walk farther. If you work at a job, set a timer to get up and walk to the cooler to get water or walk around the office a
few times throughout the day.

Find creative ways to fit exercise into your life. For example, while I am cooking dinner and waiting for things in the microwave, I am doing squats and leg lifts or crunches on the floor. I run up and down the stairs several times throughout my day. When you are waiting for your kids to come out of a martial arts class, gymnastics, ballet or etc., instead of just sitting, get up and walk around the building several times. If there are stairs in the building, walk up and down the stairs as many times as you can.

Go easy on yourself. Don't push yourself to perform and do not set lofty goals. This is not a race or a competition. This is about you moving your body every day, so you can reduce stress, stay healthy and live longer. There is no right or wrong and there is no failure. There is only learning and adjusting to reach your personal goals. Even if you don't meet your own expectations, you will still be healthier than the people sitting on their butts every day.

A few important things to know before you get started moving your body. Whenever you exercise or do a physical activity, you must drink plenty of water to stay hydrated and replace your electrolytes that you sweat out. Consider a drink like Electrolyte Plus Cardio by Dr. Sinatra. The reason I did not mention "Gatorade" or any of the drinks you see advertised on T.V. is because they have added sugars and chemicals that I do not want to put into my body. You can also make your own natural electrolyte replacement drink. Here is an awesome healthy recipe for a homemade natural electrolyte replacement drink from Wellness Mama at http://wellnessmama.com

Ingredients:
- 1 quart of liquid (options: green tea, herbal teas, coconut water, plain water, etc)
- ⅛-1/4 tsp Himalayan Sea Salt (regular table salt will work, but it doesn't have all the trace minerals)

- ¼ to ½ tsp crushed Calcium magnesium tablets or powder (optional)
- ¼ cup or more of juice (optional. Can use grape, apple, lemon, lime, pineapple, etc)
- 1-2 TBSP sweetener (optional). You can use honey, stevia, etc. I suggest brewing stevia leaf into the base liquid for the most natural option.

Instructions

Brew tea if using or slightly warm base liquid

Add sea salt and calcium magnesium (if using)

Add juice and mix or shake well

Cool and store in fridge until ready to use

Wellness Mama also mentioned that her normal recipe includes: 1 quart of tea (brewed with Red Raspberry Leaf, Alfalfa, Nettle and Stevia), ¼ tsp sea salt, ¼ tsp calcium magnesium powder (about 1,000 mg), and ¼ cup grape or apple juice.

Make sure to eat plenty of protein and get nutritional support when you are exercising. Your muscles need protein to grow stronger. You also need to stretch either during or after each exercise or activity you do. Never stretch before you work out with cold muscles or you will hurt yourself. You always want to warm up your muscles first before stretching them to avoid injuries.

Now that you know what you need to do to get your body moving and live longer, I am expecting you to start some type of exercise ASAP!

Sleep Your Way to Good Mental and Physical Health

Since problems with sleeping are one of the top symptoms of stress, most of my clients have problems sleeping at night. Many of my clients cannot sleep more than a few hours each night. I give them my sleep plan and they call me within a few days and tell me that they slept really well for the first time in years. Sleep is a double whammy, since emotional stress causes problems with your sleep, and problems sleeping causes physical and mental stress, as well as illness. [This is similar to the chronic pain cycle that I will be sharing in the next section of this chapter.] Everyone knows that stress prevents you from sleeping well at night, but there are many other things that can keep you from getting your zzzz's. Here are some of the many things that will interrupt or destroy your sleep:

Poor nutrition. Eating a poor diet and being deficient in certain vitamins and minerals can interrupt your sleep.

Eating before bedtime. Because it can take up to 4 hours for your stomach to digest food, the process of that can keep some people awake. It may also give you indigestion or a stomachache to eat at bedtime since you are laying down when your food is digesting. Another reason eating at bedtime is bad, is because some foods that you eat less than 4 hours before bedtime can turn to fat in your body, which makes you gain weight.

Caffeine. Eating too much chocolate, drinking too much coffee, tea, soda or energy drinks, taking supplements containing caffeine. Some people, like myself, are so sensitive to caffeine that any amount of this substance can keep them up all night.

Other people, like my husband, can drink a Coke and go right to bed and fall asleep. That is very rare, since caffeine is a stimulant and will usually keep you awake.

Drugs and alcohol. Whether its prescription drugs or illegal drugs like heroine, many drugs can keep you from sleeping. There are some drugs that make you fall asleep like muscle relaxers and sinus medication but usually the opposite is true. Most people think alcohol helps you fall asleep; but because it's really a stimulant, your sleep will be interrupted. This is especially true if you over-indulge.

Eating a lot of Sugar. Sugar can act like a stimulant in some people and make them hyper. Sensitive people have a greater issue with this. Usually you get a temporary hyper high with sugar and then you crash. However, if you have it before bedtime, you are going to awake for a while.

Exposure to bright lighting before bedtime. This interferes with the hormone (melatonin) and chemicals in your brain that are present when it's time to go to sleep. The bright lights send signals to your brain telling you it's time to get going.

Exercise. When you exercise, you get your blood flow and circulation moving, stimulate your brain and release hormones like adrenaline into your body that give you energy and can also make you hyper. It takes your body up to 4 hours to calm down and process the results of the exercise.

Sex. Just like exercise, there are certain chemicals released after having sex that can energize your mind and body. This one is tricky, since sex can also make you fall asleep. It depends on the person and the way you are having sex. Some sex is like a weight lifting workout and some sex is like a meditation. Depending on how you are doing it, you have the possibility of sleeping well or being wide awake all night. If you are concerned about this, just make sure to have sex earlier in the day or evening.

Getting into an argument with your spouse or someone else. One of the best ways to have your mind going all night is to go to bed angry.

Your adrenaline is pumping through your body just like you ran a marathon race. Make sure to cool your head off and calm yourself completely before heading for bed.

Watching violent T.V. shows and movies, watching horror or something complicated that stimulates your brain. Also, the lights from the television have a stimulating effect on your brain.

Exposure to cell phones, video games and computer screens within 2 – 4 hours of bedtime will keep you from sleeping. The blue lights stimulate your brain. The newest studies show that chronic bright light exposure at bedtime, like watching TV or looking at computers, raises cortisol stress hormones in the body which leads to depression. According to the National Sleep Foundation, more than 90 percent of Americans regularly use a computer or electronic device of some kind in the hour before bed. Researchers have also found that artificial light from some devices at night time can mess with your brain chemicals that promote sleep. Researchers at Rensselaer Polytechnic Institute found that exposure to light from computer tablets significantly lowered levels of the hormone melatonin, which regulates the internal clock and plays a role in your sleep cycle. This means that you can increase your chance of getting depression, if you do these activities at bedtime.

Reading educational materials at bedtime that involves complicated thinking will stimulate your brain and can keep your mind going for hours.

Are you wondering, "How much sleep do I need to have a healthy mind and body?" The National Sleep Foundation says that research cannot pinpoint an exact amount of sleep but they can give you recommended amounts or rules of thumb based on what all the experts agree upon. They say that it's important to pay attention to your own individual needs by assessing how you feel on different amounts of sleep. Here are some of the questions the NSF says to ask yourself to know how much sleep you should get:

Are you productive, healthy and happy on seven hours of sleep? Or does it take you nine hours of quality ZZZs to get you into high gear?

Do you have health issues such as being overweight? Are you at risk for any disease?

Are you experiencing sleep problems?

Do you depend on caffeine to get you through the day?

Do you feel sleepy when driving?

Here are the National Sleep Foundation's recommended amounts of sleep for each age group:

Newborns (0-3 months): Sleep range narrowed to 14-17 hours each day
Infants (4-11 months): Sleep range widened two hours to 12-15 hours
Toddlers (1-2 years): Sleep range widened by one hour to 11-14 hours
Preschoolers (3-5): Sleep range widened by one hour to 10-13 hours
School age children (6-13): Sleep range widened by one hour to 9-11 hours
Teenagers (14-17): Sleep range widened by one hour to 8-10 hours
Younger adults (18-25): Sleep range is 7-9 hours
Adults (26-64): Sleep range did not change and remains 7-9 hours
Older adults (65+): Sleep range is 7-8 hours

Many people deal with sleep problems the same way they deal with stress in their life: They either take drugs that have multiple side effects including drug addiction and memory loss or they drink alcohol. Don't do this!

I have suffered with sleep issues over the years from anxiety, worry, fears and general stress. I don't have a problem with that any more, although I will have problems sleeping from time to time if I am ill or have some pain in my body. I have experimented on myself for over 30 years with countless remedies and prescription sleep drugs. Many of them came with side effects, stomach upset and feeling like a zombie the following day. In 2012, I came up with a special sleep formula that has had no side effects for me, no addictive components, all natural and helps me sleep like a baby. The best part is no hangover, drugged out or yucky feelings the next day. Further into this section, you will find my personal herbal recipe for improving sleep.

I will now share with you my special sleep improvement program that I give to my coaching clients.

Kimberly's Sleep Improvement Program:
Things you should NEVER do, if you want to sleep:

Eating a bad diet. Many people eat lots of sugar, High Fructose Corn Syrup, processed foods, carbohydrates and other bad things. If you really want to sleep you will have to throw away your bad diet and trade it for a healthy diet. Also, make sure to and take plenty of vitamins and minerals

Never eat a meal right before you go to sleep. Try to eat no closer than 4 hours before bedtime unless you eat a very light snack like the ones I mention below, or you have to eat something for the purpose of taking medication or your doctor has instructed you to do so because of a medical issue.

If you are sensitive to caffeine and have problems sleeping at night, stop eating or drinking any substances with caffeine. If you are someone who has no problem at all with caffeine, the rule is to cut off your caffeine at 2:00 p.m. According to a report in Psychology Today, late-afternoon caffeine can cause problems for your sleep, even if you aren't aware of it.

To avoid sleep disruption, restrict your caffeine consumption primarily to the morning hours. If you do have a midday cup of coffee, make sure to drink it before 2 p.m. The report also said to taper caffeine as the day progresses. Start your day with your most highly caffeinated beverage and ease up on the caffeine as the morning goes on.

First thing in the morning is likely when you'll crave caffeine the most, and when it can do you the most good in terms of boosting energy and shaking off the effects of a night's sleep. Switch over to tea or decaffeinated coffee as the morning continues, to keep overall daily caffeine amounts moderate and be comfortably caffeine-free by mid-afternoon.

Avoid drugs that keep you awake and alcohol as much as possible. Never eat sugary foods or drink sugar filled beverages at bedtime and minimize sugar consumption during the day.

Do not use bright lights right before bed time, instead use candles or soft lighting to calm down and send signals to your brain that it's time for bed soon.

Try not to exercise within the last 4 hours before you go to sleep. If you can exercise first thing in the morning, lunchtime or right after you get off from work, it would be better for your sleep.

Never go to sleep angry and if you do get into an argument with someone or have angry feelings in the evening, make sure you allow yourself time to cool off before you hit the hay.

Minimize or do not watch violent TV shows and movies right before you plan to sleep. Also any type of movie or TV show that causes you to get emotionally upset, sad or angry is best avoided at bedtime.

Keep all electronic devices including cell phones, computers, notepads and video screens away from your bed while you are sleeping, or make sure that they are turned off. Also, turn off your devices and stop looking at them at least 2 to 4 hours before you go to sleep at night.

Do not read books or magazines that stimulate your brain and get you thinking (or angry) before bedtime. Instead read easy books like humor, comics, adventure, romance, travel, biography, autobiography and art.

Things you can try out to help you sleep better:

Learn to manage stress by reading this book and implementing what you have learned. Stress is the number one thing that prevents people from sleeping.

Stick to a regular sleep schedule, even on weekends. Your body has a special circadian rhythm and when you wake up at different times on different days or go to sleep much later on weekends, it disrupts your body's natural circadian rhythm.

Make sure the temperature in your bedroom is always comfortable. If your air is too dry, use a humidifier. If your room is too hot or too cold, you will have difficulty sleeping at night.

Sleep on a comfortable mattress and use comfortable pillows. Also make sure your sheets and blankets are comfortable as well.

Try to sleep in a quiet place and minimize noise. If you have a spouse who snores, a noisy refrigerator or air conditioning, use ear plugs.

Try playing soft music at bedtime. Classical music, new age music and meditation music are good for falling asleep.

Listen to a guided sleep hypnosis audio before going to sleep □ Do a relaxation yoga or stretching video.

Practice meditation right before bedtime.

Breathing exercises. My son had insomnia and I taught him a simple breathing exercise to do when he went to sleep at night. After a few nights of practicing the breathing he was out cold and has never had a problem since. Here is the simple breath exercise I taught my son and you can try for yourself:

Lie down in bed, flat on your back. Make sure you have a comfortable pillow and your spine is straight. Place your arms comfortably at your sides.

Next, focus all your attention on the breath going in and out of your nose. Focus on the feeling of it and the sound of the breath. When you breathe in, think to yourself the word "in". When you breathe out, think to yourself the word, "out".

After you have done this for a few minutes, you should fall asleep. If not you can try the other suggestions in this section.

Exercise is paramount to better health and better sleep, but make sure to exercise every day during the day time. It will tire your body so you can sleep better at night.

It also gives you feel good chemicals like serotonin for your brain, which also improves sleep. Move your body frequently throughout the day. When you sit around all of the time, your body will never get tired and it makes it much harder to fall asleep.

Take a hot bubble bath, hot shower, or sit in a hot tub or sauna before you go to bed. The warmth relaxes all of your muscles and takes away the tension. Make sure to drink plenty of water.

Use modalities like massage, acupuncture, Reiki, therapeutic touch, acupressure and etc. to help you sleep better at night. Many of my clients report sleeping better when they get modalities like massage and acupuncture.

Right before you go to bed, eat a light snack of foods that help you to sleep better. These are foods that have chemicals that are released into your brain and help you to sleep:

Bananas – (have tryptophan) o One cup of warm milk - "My 89 year old mother in law swears by a banana and warm milk every night at bedtime to help her sleep."

Turkey – (has tryptophan)   o 1 ounce of tart cherry juice (has melatonin)

During the day eat high fiber foods to regulate your blood sugar and prevent sleep disturbances.

Try supplements at bedtime that can help you sleep better:

Natural Calm (magnesium citrate) – This is a powder drink that you can buy in plain, lemon, orange and other flavors and mix it up with warm water and drink like a tea at bedtime. Follow directions on the jar. If you don't want to take Natural Calm, you can take magnesium citrate capsules at bedtime.

DO NOT TAKE MAGNESIUM SUPPLEMENTS AT THE SAME TIME AS PRESCRIPTION DRUGS, IT CAN BLOCK THE ABSORBTION OF THE MEDICINE. Always start off with a small dose of 150 mg and work up to 500 mg because magnesium can give you diarrhea.

Melatonin o Chamomile tea o Lemon Balm (Melissa Officianalis) o Passionflower (passiflora) o Valerian.

Be careful with valerian dosing because it can upset your stomach. o Hops

Essential oils are very beneficial – The best are lavender and Roman Chamomile; diffusing Jasmine oil before bedtime can also help you to fall asleep and stay asleep longer. You can use these in a diffuser or mix the oils with water and spray on your pillow case and sheets. You can also put a dab of oil on your wrist.

Warning**
If you try everything in this program and still cannot sleep, please see a doctor. You may have something more serious wrong with you than just basic stress, pain or worry keeping you up at night. You could have a hormonal imbalance. I know many women who cannot sleep because menopausal hot flashes are keeping them awake at night. They finally find relief after their physician checks their hormones and puts them on bio-identical hormones or special herbal supplements.

The Chronic Pain Cycle

One of the worst types of physical stress is pain, especially chronic daily pain. If you have chronic pain and don't manage it, you can get stuck in the chronic stress cycle. When you get injured or have pain from some other source like rheumatoid arthritis, you can be trapped like a hamster on a wheel. Some people never get off of this wheel and suffer for many years.

Physical Stress caused by Accident, injury or chronic disease

Causes Pain and discomfort

Causes Emotional stress (anxiety, depression, anger, resentment & more)

Causes mental illness and Health problems

Causes More Pain and discomfort

Causes More emotional stress

Start all over again

You can avoid getting stuck in the chronic pain cycle by learning to prevent, manage and heal your pain. You cannot prevent all of the types of pain you may have in your life, especially the pain you get when you have an injury to your body. However, there are some types of pain you can prevent and you can also prevent some injury. Here are some of the many ways you can prevent some types of pain:

Eat a healthy anti-inflammatory diet

Keep your muscles and bones strong with healthy diet, vitamins, minerals and supplements. Check with a holistic doctor to find out which ones are best for you

Exercise daily to strengthen your body; strong muscles will protect you from injury and help you bounce back quicker if you do get an injury. I recommend Miranda Esmonde White's Aging Backwards program and her Classical Stretch Program. I use this myself every week and have noticed a huge improvement in my strength, flexibility and balance. http://classicalstretch.com/

Work on improving your balance so you don't fall

Keep your body flexible by regular stretching or yoga. It's harder to get injured and create pain when your body is flexible.

Take vitamins, minerals and supplements that support your body and keep your bones and muscle tissue healthy. Some of the most important ones are vitamin C, Vitamin D3, Vitamin K, calcium, potassium and magnesium. Stinging nettle has been used by Native Americans for hundreds of years as a bone strengthening tea because it contains tons of minerals and nutrients. Check with your doctor to find out the appropriate amount of vitamins and minerals for your body. Be careful not to overdose. You should also get blood tests to find out where you may have deficiencies.

Keep hydrated. Some pain, like muscle spasms, are caused by not drinking enough water.

Many people have more accidents and injuries when they tired or when they are emotionally stressed, so make sure to get 8 hours of sleep and learn how to manage emotional stress (which you will learn a little about in Chapter 3). We all have hurt ourselves by bumping into objects, dropping things, trips and falls, when we are tired or upset about something.

Here are some of the many natural ways you can manage or heal your pain, without drugs, cortisol injections or surgery:

Eat a healthy anti-inflammatory Diet

Take anti-inflammatory supplements like flax oil, fish oil, Bromelain, turmeric, resveratrol, pygnogenal, boswelia, borage oil, cayenne pepper, cat's claw, devil's claw, ginger, MSM, glucosamine, white Willow Bark, Pau D' Arco, quercetin and green tea. – Make sure to check with your doctor first before taking any supplements.

Topical pain creams, gels or lotions. There are many on the market and some are made with very potent herbs that are great for pain. There are also some topical pain products that contain certain mineral compounds like magnesium or silica that are helpful.

Use heat or ice depending on the type of injury or pain. Check with your doctor because you can make an injury or pain worse if you don't use the correct temperature.

Go to practitioners to get pain relief modalities. Some of the many good pain relief modalities include acupuncture, chiropractic, massage, acupressure, cranial sacral, physical therapy, ultrasound, electric stimulation, hyperbaric chamber, Fisher-Wallace equipment and more.

Get 8 hours of sleep each night – Your body does most of its healing and repair while you are sleeping

Learn how to practice Mindfulness. I am a Certified Mindfulness Instructor and have been practicing and teaching this awesome mind activity for 13 years. It has helped me get through tons of injuries and flair ups of tendonitis, tendinosis, bursitis and joint pain and mindfulness has helped me to keep my sanity. Mindfulness helps you to control your mind so that you don't experience the mental stress associated with pain that puts you into the Chronic Pain Cycle shown in the chart.

Reprogramming your mind for positive thoughts and getting rid of fears. The more negative thoughts you think, the more your pain will stay around or increase.

Healing mantras. You are co-creator of your life and whatever you think or believe in your mind and whatever you say with your mouth is what you will receive. Therefore, using phrases (I am healthy and whole; I am perfect health; My body is getting stronger and healthier every day; Each and every day I get better and better) will help your body to heal quicker. Whatever you think or say, your body follows.

Use energy healing modalities like Reiki, Qi Gong, Pranic Healing, Quantum Touch, Chakra balancing, BodyTalk, body codes, healing codes, Psych-K and others.

Other Ideas for Managing Physical Stress

Part of living longer and healthier includes getting annual or bi-annual preventative checkups and blood tests with an MD, D.O. or Naturopath. When doctors look you over regularly and give you important tests, they are able to find everything from cancers and diseases to vitamin or nutrient deficiencies. If you catch these things early, you can take care of them and hopefully get rid of the issues before they become life threatening. Some people don't go to doctors for regular check-ups and then are perplexed when they get diagnosed with

"Stage 4" cancer. With regular exams, cancers can be caught early, when many interventions exist to get rid of it and live longer, healthier.

It is very important for you to know that merely feeling good does not mean that you are healthy. I have had many friends in tell me they never go for checkups, because they feel good. Unfortunately, some of the most serious illnesses have no warnings or side effects. Cancer and heart attack are a few of those. Also, vitamin and other deficiencies can lead to serious health problems. If you have iron deficiency, low thyroid, vitamin B12 or even a vitamin D deficiency, it can be dangerous and kill you.

I believe it's important to get regular adjustments with a really good chiropractor. Your spine is important, because if it's out of alignment, you can have everything from problems with your nerves and organs to issues with chronic pain. I personally had problems breathing a few times because I had pulled a few ribs and my chiropractor was able to put them back where they belong so I could breathe again. I have been seeing a chiropractor since my college years and they have helped me heal from many injuries over the years. If you have any muscle imbalances, your spine can go out of alignment. A chiropractor can check you to see if you have any imbalances.

We don't realize that the type of shoes we wear can stress out our bodies by causing muscle imbalances, spinal miss-alignments and other problems. It is important to wear good supportive shoes. If you have flat feet, it can also cause problems with your back and body, so it's important to have your feet checked and get orthotics if you need them. My chiropractor has a machine in his office to check your arch and gait. I found out that I had long flat arches and my gait was off, which was causing my pelvis to tilt and spine to go out of alignment. Once I got custom orthotics, I was able to get my body back in place again and had much less hip pain.

One of the most important exams that people forget is regular dental exams. Even though it is stressful for many people to go to the dentist, it is one of those things that you have to do to live longer. Some of you may be thinking, "I can live a long life without my teeth." The reason that dental exams are important, is because gum disease (gingivitis) can cause heart disease and heart attack, because infected gums are a source of inflammation! I have a very good friend whose husband did not take care of himself and go to the doctor or dentist. As a result, he got a gum infection and it went into his blood, down to his heart and he died. My dentist uses state of the art equipment in her office and one of the things she does is take a slide of your saliva and test it to see if harmful bacteria is in your mouth. If you have the bad bacteria forms, she has you do a special protocol where you brush and floss every day with a special solution for a few weeks and then they re-check your gums to see if the bad bugs were killed. If you don't have luck killing the bad bacteria, they have to do periodontal work on you to get your gums healthy again. She believes that she is saving many people from future heart attacks by killing the bad mouth bugs, before they kill her patients.

If you want healthy teeth and gums, you need to get rid of the plaque-causing bacteria. The best way to do that is to use a good toothbrush at least two times a day and floss your teeth every day. Xylitol is great for preventing cavities and gum disease. It also tastes great. There are many gums, candies, toothpastes and other products with Xylitol in them.

My family and I have been using the Sonicare toothbrush for many years. It has cut down on the number of cavities we get and made our dental cleanings quicker and easier. If you have never tried one of the plug-in mechanical wonders before, I highly recommend that you try one of them; there are many good brands!

Make sure that when you choose a dentist, they use mercury-free. Mercury is a neurotoxin that is harmful to your brain, your reproductive system and your entire body. Most dentists don't use it anymore, but it's worth checking. Also, make sure that if you get any filling removed which contains mercury, you use a dentist who knows safe procedures for removing them without you having to breathe in the dust. I will talk more about this in Chapter 4.

Last Words of Wisdom

Some last words of wisdom about physical stress: do your best to keep yourself and your family healthy with proper diet, vitamins and sleep to keep your immune system strong. Also, managing emotional stress, which we will discuss in Chapter 3, is important for keeping a strong immune system. If you or a family member does get sick with a virus, bacterial infection, disease or any other health problem, try to use natural remedies whenever possible like vitamins, supplements, herbs, oils, holistic modalities or energy healing. If you have to use prescription drugs, proceed with caution. Prescription (RX) drugs can have side effects. Make sure you talk to your pharmacist about any side effects or contraindications that the RX may have and get educated so you know what to expect. Don't depend on your M.D. to know these things. Most MDs have no training in the areas of biochemistry and pharmacology, and do not know the details about the drugs you are receiving. Some doctors may not know if the drug interacts badly with other things you are taking, so it's good to talk with the pharmacist about that. I always look in a PDR (Physician's Desk Reference) before taking any drugs I have never used before. I also have a great relationship with my pharmacist and ask her many questions. Don't be afraid to ask!

Take control of your health by practicing prevention. I'm sure you have heard the saying, "An ounce of prevention is worth a pound of cure." Every day you should be doing things to stay healthy. We already talked about diet, supplements and exercise.

You can also read some of the many hundreds of self-healing, diet and health books that have been published. Consider getting a subscription to health magazine that will give you regular tips for staying healthy. Some of the ones I like are: Men's Health, Prevention, Health Magazine, Women's Health and Consumer Reports.

Do regular research on the internet to look up subjects that are important to your health. Watch good-quality TV programs on health. If you have a local PBS channel, you can find all sorts of health and exercise shows, including a show called "In Close". Some of the many physical health experts who have programs on PBS include JJ. Virgin, Dr. Daniel Amen, Dr. Joel Fuhrman, Brenda Watson, Dr. Christiane Northrup and more. PBS also features many exercise shows to help you stay in shape.

There are also medical shows on T.V. and even the local news shows have health reporters. My favorite preventative medical show to watch on TV is the Dr. Oz Show with Mehmet Oz, M.D. The thing I love about Doctor Oz is he practices what he preaches to others. He actually follows his own advice, takes great care of himself and his family and he always looks healthy and happy.

One of the most important things you need to learn to have a longer life, is how to have body awareness and tune into your body. Many people walk around with their body and mind separated in such a way, that they have all sorts of serious health things going on, like cancer and lime disease and don't even know it. Don't be clueless about your body unless you have a death wish. You can heal some very deadly illnesses like Lyme disease, cancer and Type 2 Diabetes, if you are fully aware of what is going on in your body at all times.

I constantly hear stories of people who have very bad symptoms like continuous vomiting and when they finally go to a doctor, they find out they have stage 4 pancreatic cancer or some other type of cancer that has metastasized. That was the case for my own mother who was so busy taking care of everyone else that she ignored her own body and the symptoms. The signs were there all along and if she had paid more attention to the signs her body was giving her and went to a doctor right away, she might have been able to heal her cancer or at least live a little longer.

I have also heard stories of women who were pregnant and didn't know it and gave birth in the bathroom toilet. With all of the symptoms that happen with pregnancy, besides putting on weight, how could someone not know they are pregnant? The only thing that makes sense to me is that they are constantly ignoring their body. They have what I call a major mind/body disconnect. When you experience health problems or even mild symptoms in your body, listen to your body and either go to a doctor or at the very least research the symptoms on the web and then decide if you want to see a doctor.

It is so important to always have your brain and body linked together as one. Unfortunately, when your brain is impacted by emotional stress, feeling overwhelmed or just busy with thoughts, your mind and body become disconnected. It is important for you to pay attention and really take notes in the next chapter on emotional stress and start working on managing your emotional stress, so your body and brain can connect properly. You can also create better body awareness and a great mind/body connection by quieting your mind everyday through a practice of meditation, prayer, mindfulness, yoga, tai chi or other mind/body methods. After practicing mindfulness for many years, my doctor has told me that I had the best body awareness of any of her patients, because I always know when something is wrong and I also know what I need to do to heal.

You can do this too and it's very simple. When you first start practicing mind body techniques like meditation, you will really notice what we call in mindfulness, the "monkey mind," which is all of the thoughts running wild in your head. Over time of practicing mind body techniques like mindfulness or meditation, your monkey mind will calm down and you will have thoughts that jump around a lot less. You will start to notice your body more and more and eventually you will link your mind and body as one. It only takes a little time every day and you will live longer and healthier too.

If and when you are diagnosed with a mental or physical illness or problem, do not expect that your doctor will heal you. It is up to you to heal yourself by using whatever modalities, foods, supplements or methods necessary. Also, never let any doctor tell you that there is no cure for what you have and that you are doomed. In most cases, you are able to heal yourself. Hundreds of books have been written about self-healing. God created your body to naturally heal itself and God also created thousands of plants, foods, medical modalities, people, energy and other things that can heal you. I believe there is a cure on earth for just about anything. Some of them may not have been discovered yet, but they are out there.

The most important factor that keeps your body from healing itself is stress. If you read this book and start managing all of the stress in your life, you should be able to heal better. Please keep in mind that there are times when managing stress and doing everything you can is just not enough. I have known people who did everything right including eating well, taking care of themselves, feeling happy and managing stress, exercising and they still got cancer and died. In their case, it was just their time to go and there is nothing you can do when it's your time. However, you should not be concerned with that now and only focus on the positive and trying to heal yourself. This is why it's so important for you to learn how to quiet your mind and create a healthy mind/body connection.

Once you can quiet your mind, you can tune into your body and ask your body what it needs to heal. Emotional stress from all of life's situations prevents your body from naturally healing itself. When you ask yourself what your body needs to heal, it will be a combination of the list of things that you already know about, like changing your diet and a list of emotional stressors that you need to heal. I will cover be covering emotions in the next chapter. After you have asked your body what it needs, sit down and write up a plan to heal your body. Here is an example of a healing plan you can write for yourself:

My Healing Plan

For any health issue you have in your life, here is my personal healing plan that I have always used and recommend to clients.

- ➢ Go to holistic or functional medicine doctor and get tested, diagnosed treatment, medicine, etc. If they cannot diagnose you then see a medical intuitive.
- ➢ Think only positive thoughts and speak only positive things
- ➢ Eat better healthy diet and drink plenty of filtered water daily
- ➢ Exercise every day
- ➢ Take vitamins and supplements for healing
- ➢ Have a Reiki session or other type of energy healing sessions
- ➢ Get out of debt – Money is one of top stressors for all humans
- ➢ Change jobs if you don't love what you do and who you do it with – You need to be fully aligned with your purpose when doing a business, career or job and if you are not you will never be happy. I have been helping clients figure out their purpose and help them with career or business decisions since 1996

> ➤ Get rid of bad relationships – Toxic relationships will suck all your energy and make you stressed out and unhappy.
> ➤ Get more sleep – Adults need at least 7 hours of sleep each night
> ➤ Read health and wellness books and magazines and watch health videos
> ➤ Have a daily spiritual practice and connect with Mother Father Source, Creator, God

When you write your healing plan, be as thorough as possible. Spend time on the internet researching what you have been diagnosed with on reputable medical sites and find healing ideas that resonate with you and feel safe. Make sure to never use any experimental or dangerous products or modalities that have not been around long enough to have a safety track record or that have not been tested and proven safe and effective!

When It Is Time to Call a Medical Intuitive

If you have tried everything you can to heal yourself from an illness or a chronic health problem, including reading and following through with this book and nothing seems to work, you may want to work with a Medical Intuitive. Also, if you go to a doctor or you have seen several doctors and they cannot diagnose you, then you may want to work with Medical Intuitive. Another reason to see a Medical Intuitive is if you want help and guidance with healing but do not want to see any doctors. A Medical Intuitive is a person who has intuitive gifts and sometimes other gifts and who uses them to find out the root cause of your health problems and provides guidance for healing.

Some Medical Intuitives can scan you like an x-ray machine and others may use things like energy testing, insight, channeling, prophecy or other spiritual gifts to help you out. I thank God for the intuitive gifts he gave me and use a combination of channeling, intuition and energy scanning to help my clients find the root cause of their health problems. Once I find the root cause, I can advise them on steps to heal which many times includes sending my clients to M.D.'s, N.D.'s, chiropractors or different alternative healthcare professionals for treatment and testing.

If you decide to seek out a medical intuitive, please be careful because there are many charlatans and scammers in the intuitive and psychic/medium industry. What you want to look for is a person with many years of experience, a list of references that you can call, list of testimonials, good reputation on the internet and you have to feel comfortable with them. I personally have had to go to a Medical Intuitive for my own health problems, because people with spiritual gifts are unable to see their own problems and have to seek out help. Also, we all need each other and have to be able to receive what we give out. As a healer, I seek out other healers to help me. Of course, I found many scammers and fakes. One of the best medical intuitives I have seen is Carolyn Myss.

Activities to start managing physical stress

Create a "Move Your Body" plan for daily exercise. Spend at least 10 minutes to 1 hour each day doing an exercise of your choice that you enjoy and that is good for your experience level. Make sure that the exercise is not over your head and pick something different every day, so you do not get bored and quit. For example, if you like to walk, swim, and ride your bike, then do each one of those on a different day.

If you cannot find time to exercise, make an effort to set a timer for once every hour and get up from your chair and walk around the building for a minute or two or go get some water. Put on a wearable monitoring product like FitBit or wear a pedometer and start moving every day.

Keep pain under control so you don't get stuck in chronic pain/stress cycle. See my recommendations on pain from this chapter to find out what you need to do and then sit down and write out a pain management plan for yourself. Make sure to post it somewhere that you will see it daily. When we write down goals or instructions and look at them every day, it makes it easier and quicker to accomplish the goals.

Using the information from this chapter, take a few minutes to write down the top 3 things that you would like to change in your life right now. Then write down some action items for how you will create these changes.

For example: Item 1 – using the computer close to bedtime. Action Item for change: turn off computer every night at 7:00 p.m.

Item 2 – Research Anti-inflammatory diet. Action Item for change: Start implementing my new diet each day in gradually with the old one.

CHAPTER 3
EMOTIONAL STRESS

O f all of the types of stress, emotional stress creates the most illness and death; it destroys lives, businesses, careers and relationships. Many studies have shown that emotional stress causes between 75% and 98% of all illness. A study by the American Medical Association (AMA) found that stress causes at least 75% of the illnesses and diseases that doctors see. The International Agency for Research on Cancer and the World Health Organization have both concluded that 80% of cancers are due to lifestyles and are not genetic. They say this is a conservative number. According to Dr. Bruce Lipton (The Biology of Belief, 2008), genetic disorders like Huntington's chorea, beta thalassemia, cystic fibrosis, as well as inherited cancers and other inherited diseases, affect less than 2% of the population. He says a staggering 98% of diseases are based on lifestyle choices and therefore, thinking. Dr. Brian Luke Seaward says that the association between stress and disease is 85%. When I asked some of the physicians I work with how many patients were seeing them for stress related health problems, every doctor I spoke with believed that 100% of their patients had stress-related health problems. Seeing that 90% of doctors suffer from emotional stress, it makes complete sense.

Many of the experts are focusing on just one type of emotional stress, so-called conscious emotional stress. But there are four types of emotional stress that you need to manage if you want to live longer. The four types of emotional stress are: conscious emotional stress, subconscious emotional stress, inherited epigenetic stress and past life emotional Stress.

In this chapter I will discuss each of these four types of emotional stress and give you some tips for how to manage them. Emotional stress is a complicated subject and each person is unique, so it's not possible to cover everything you need to know about emotional stress in this one book. This chapter focuses on the most important information you need to know to get started healing and managing emotional stress.

Once you have mastered this information, you can spend time researching additional information on your own or you can see me or some other coach to give you customized assistance for your unique situation.

As you read through the chapter, you will probably find at least one or more of the emotional stress topics that apply to you. While reading this chapter, you may want to highlight the sections that apply to you or have a note pad and pen to write down the most important points. This will really help you when you do the activities at the end of this chapter and, of course, at end of the book. Please avoid judging and criticizing yourself, and do not worry about what other people may think. No one is going to see this information except for you (and possibly your coach or counselor). The more you are able to acknowledge and accept your stress and take responsibility for it, the quicker you will be able to start healing and managing your emotional stress.

One word of caution before starting this chapter: Please keep an open mind, because I will be discussing a few topics that some people do not believe in due to their religious training or may be thought of as taboo in some cultures. I totally respect everyone's beliefs and way to the truth; however, I am expressing my freedom of speech and beliefs in this book by sharing with you what I have learned, know and believe. I don't expect you to agree with me on everything or expect you to adopt my beliefs. However, if you really want to improve your life, you know that you have to keep an open mind and be willing to listen to new information. Some of you will read this information and say to yourself, "I know that already." If that happens to be you, then that's great. If it doesn't resonate with you, then that's okay too. I am a spiritual teacher who never judges. We all have our own way to the truth and we are each on our own unique journey.

Conscious Emotional Stress

The best way to explain Conscious Emotional Stress is that it consists of all of the negative thoughts, feelings, emotions, beliefs, ideas, values, opinions, attitudes, perceptions and reactions that we have 100% control over. We are fully conscious of them. If I were to ask you, "Do you worry?" and you say, "Yes, I worry," then you are fully conscious of that. According to the New York Times on line health guide, emotional stress can come from any situation or thought that makes you feel frustrated, angry, or anxious. What is stressful to you may not be stressful to another person.

You create your conscious stress and in many cases your perceptions determine what you label as stressful or not stressful. Emotional stress can be caused by many thousands of different stimuli. For some it could be the death of a friend or relative and for others it can be a difficult relationship at home or work. Various emotions like anger, sadness, despair, unhappiness, hostility, un-forgiveness, chronic worry, grudges, anxiety, depression and fear can cause chronic emotional stress. Emotional stress is also caused by negative thinking and beliefs about yourself and the world around you. People who are always positive and happy are less subject to stress-induced illness than negative thinkers.

In order to manage emotional stress, you need to first accept the fact that you create most of the stress in your life - and take full responsibility for it. According to the science of Quantum Physics, Quantum Entrainment and Energy Medicine, your thoughts, emotions and even your speech have either a negative or positive charge. This charge or energy frequency not only affects you, but affects everyone and everything around you. This same information was written 2,000 years ago in the Bible and has been taught in other religions as well.

You are actually creating your life and influencing those around you with your thoughts, emotions and words. Most of conscious emotional

THE REAL FOUNTAIN OF YOUTH | 117

stress is caused by what I call Stinking Thinking or negative thoughts. As I mentioned earlier, every time you think negative thoughts or say negative words, you are releasing stress hormones into your body which cause illness. Those thoughts have a low or negative energy vibration or frequency that also harms your spiritual body and your mental body as well as your physical body.

What many people don't know about conscious emotional stress, is that it starts from the minute you are born. The stress caused by our thoughts, beliefs, perceptions, opinions and behavior has been influenced by our parents, other family members, friends, neighbors, teachers, co-workers, our environment, culture, society, social media, other media, books and games. Everything and everyone has an impact on how you form your thoughts and your belief systems. When the stimulus going into your brain is negative, then what comes out is negative too. The opposite is true as well. Positive information coming into your brain, equals positive info circulating in your brain and going out. If your parents and other people around you when you were growing up were always negative, then chances are you are going to be negative, too.

My parents were both very negative people who worried about everything. Even though I was fairly positive on my own, my parents' negativity affected me as well and dragged me down. As a result of my parents' negativity, I suffered with many years of anxiety and fears. My spiritual path turned me around and now I can teach others how to get out of that negative rut. When you surround yourself with negative friends, not only will they suck your energy down, but they may unconsciously influence you to become negative. Once I healed myself from all my parents' influence, I got rid of all of my negative and energy vampire friends, because I choose to hang out with people who are positive.

Do you remember the Chronic Pain/Stress Cycle? Well, there is a Chronic Illness/Emotional Stress Cycle as well. When you have emotional stress, you get health problems and more pain. When you get health problems and pain, you get more emotional stress. Before you know it, you are stuck in a cycle of chronic suffering worse than anything the Buddha could have imagined three thousand years ago. The Buddha believed that we create our suffering through our wants and desires and that when we give them up, we do not suffer. I believe that our wants and desires cause only a small part of our suffering.

There are thousands of other things that cause suffering, and negative thinking is the tip of the iceberg. My truth about suffering is you don't have to accept it or put up with it. You are in control of your mind and your feelings and can learn how to manage stress. To help you start managing Conscious Emotional Stress, I will dedicate the rest of this chapter section to the major types of conscious emotional stress and what you can do to manage them.

Please remember that your emotional stress did not happen overnight; it happened over the course of your entire life, so it will take some time to manage it. Because there is no magic wand to wave and make your troubles go away, success will take hard work and effort on your part. However, if you start implementing the information contained here, do more research and work on yourself, you can create the happy life you deserve.

Negative Thoughts (Stinking Thinking)
Over 85% of most people's thoughts are negative. According to the science of Quantum Physics, the negative energy of your thoughts not only harms your body, mind and spirit, but it also acts as a magnet and attracts negative things into your life. The good news is that your brain is like a computer and you can program your brain for positive thinking,

which I will talk more about in a moment. First, I would like to consider the five main types of negative thoughts:

Negative thoughts about yourself
Negative thoughts about other people, places, things and events.
Negative belief systems
Having unreasonable expectations
Limiting yourself and others

It is easy in our society to think negative thoughts about yourself. Your self-awareness and self-esteem are impacted daily by your family, friends, society, media, and multiple other factors. If you lack self-love, you will have a tendency towards thinking negative thoughts about yourself. Our society puts pressures and expectations on us to be perfect in every way and, if we think we have failed in any way, we critique ourselves unfairly. When you are perfectionist or have unreasonable expectations of yourself, it feeds the negative selftalk (ego) with ammunition that harms your body, mind and spirit.

When people have low self-esteem or are unhappy in any way, they are also more likely to say negative things about others and about everything in their environment. Haven't you noticed that? Some of these negative thoughts of others include judgements and criticism. Whether you judge or criticize someone or something, out loud or in your mind, you are creating low energy vibration that harms you as well as the person you are judging and criticizing. You are also pulling farther and farther away from your creator when you judge and criticize because the Creator (Universal Energy) is composed of unconditional love. There is no judgment or criticism, only love. If you are someone who is trying to have a closer relationship with God, you are destroying that relationship every time you criticize or judge, either out loud or in your mind. The truth is that every person on earth is not only connected to you, but a reflection of an aspect of you. If you look at someone and don't see what you want, look inward. Chances are there is something negative about yourself that you are finding in this other person. Psychologists call this projection.

Just like the rest of Conscious Emotional Stress, negative belief systems are formed from the moment you are in the womb and created by everyone and everything in your environment. The biggest contributors to negative beliefs are your parents, other family members and teachers since they have the most influence and impact on the molding of your young mind. If you had a parent who believed that money is the root of all evil and they mentioned this to you, then you may also have that belief. If you had a school teacher who told you, "You are a stupid and cannot learn anything," then you will believe you are stupid and cannot learn anything. Negative beliefs are basically a series of lies that people have been feeding to you like candy and you have eaten it up and adopted their "lies" as your own thinking. These negative beliefs form blocks to happiness and success in your life. If you have a negative belief about money, it will block your ability to make money. If you have a negative belief about people or relationships, it will block your sabotage your ability to have happy relationships.

Having unreasonable expectations of yourself, anyone else or anything, will set you up for failure, stress and unhappiness. If others have high expectations of you, it will also cause emotional stress as you try to jump through hoops, trying to please them. Life is full of disappointments and we can never have every one of our expectations met. No person or situation is perfect and neither are you. Having unreasonably- high expectations of yourself will make you stressed and physically sick. You will never be able to meet the expectations you set up for yourself. If you have unreasonable expectations of others, they will never meet those expectations and you will be let down. If other people are unreasonable, they too will be let down, causing more emotional stress for you.

Human beings have a tendency to limit themselves and also place limits on others. From the moment you are born, people have been telling you things like:

Don't waste your time doing that, you will never be successful
That won't work out for you
Don't try to do that because you can't
You don't have the skills or knowledge to do that

We also say these limiting things to other people. Because of all the people limiting you from birth, you may now have developed a habit of limiting yourself and having limiting beliefs about yourself, others and the world. If you want to help other people to have better lives, stop saying anything negative or limiting to them about anything. If you want to have a happier and more successful life, stop thinking and saying limiting statements. Limiting thoughts and beliefs are blocks to your health and to your success in life. The truth is, we are all limitless beings. Since we co-create our lives with God, based on everything we believe, think, say and do, we can do just about anything we put our minds too. You have a brain in your head that is capable of learning and doing much more than you give yourself credit for. Humans only use less than a third of their brains and the exceptional people on the planet like Albert Einstein use more of their brain.
Since I was a small child, people have always told me that I could not do something. Every time someone has said that to me, I have proved them wrong. When I was two years out of college, I had a job selling display advertising for a conglomerate of six coastal town newspapers. The first day on the job, the old veteran salesman took me around my new territory to introduce me to business owners who were regular advertising clients. When we were in one of the businesses, I saw a little store a few shops down and said to my sales buddy, "Why don't we go in there and sell them an ad space?" The veteran salesman said to me,

"Don't waste your time going in there, they never buy anything." I took that as a challenge, because I knew that this guy had his way of selling and I had mine. I also had a mother who told me that I can do anything I put my mind to. I walked into that store and sold the owner a big display advertisement, right in front of my sales buddy. He was in complete shock. When we left that place, he said to me, "I don't understand why and how you were able to sell them." I looked at him and I said, "Well, you don't know what I am capable of and I can do anything I put my mind to." This reminds me of one of my favorite sayings:

"With God, all things are possible"

If any or all of these types of negative thinking or what I call Stinking Thinking have hit a hot button for you then I am glad you are reading this book, because you will love my advice on how to reprogram your brain for happiness and success:

The best way to get started reprogramming your mind for positive thinking is to start paying attention to your inner dialogue. Pay attention to all the conversations you have with yourself in your mind and the thoughts that pop into your head throughout the day. When you catch yourself thinking a negative thought of any kind, tell yourself, "Stop! I will no longer think this way!"

Try to come up with an opposite positive thought to counteract the negative one. For example, when you tell yourself, "My body is fat," counter that thought with "I am fine just the way I am." Another example is, "I hate my neighbor. He is such a jerk." Try to replace that with something like, "All of my relationships with my neighbors are peaceful and friendly."

You need to come up with replacement thoughts for all of your negative thinking. Every time you catch yourself thinking a negative thought, stop yourself and immediately say something in your mind that is opposite. This will also cancel out any harmful negative energy. If you start doing this every day, over time you will go from negative thinking to positive thinking. If this is too hard for you to do on your own, you may consider having a life coach help you.

Start making an effort to refrain from judging or criticizing yourself or others. Every person is on their own unique path in the universe and no one is better than another. You cannot change other people or their behavior; you can only be the change that you want to see in the world. Start practicing the art of Allowing. Try to just allow people

to be who and what they are and make the mistakes they will make without judgement or criticism. Try to see the good in everyone and everything, instead of focusing on the bad aspects. If you are focusing on the negative, you are going to have a tendency to be more judgmental and critical of others. Instead try refocusing your mind on something positive about everything and everyone in your environment. Stop criticizing yourself and learn to love yourself just the way you are. Self-criticism is self-destructive.

How many times have you felt stress when someone has criticized you? When others judge or criticize in a negative way or are trying to be mean, don't ever take it personally. Most of the time, the people criticizing you don't really know you and are not in a position to give you useful feedback. Also, if someone judges or criticizes you and you take their information in a negative manner, you are releasing cortisol and negative energy that may cause you mental and physical health problems.

There are times when people with specific expertise give you constructive criticism that they intend to help you. If the source of the criticism is someone who knows what they are talking about and who wants to help you learn and grow, then accept the information as a positive tool for your growth. However, next time a boss, friend, co-worker or other person criticizes you, insults you, or gives you an opinion that you did not ask for, carefully consider the source of the information. In many cases, the person giving you the opinion or criticism is not as knowledgeable as you on the subject! They might even be jealous of you.

Some people who criticize are just Know It All's. Some of the people who are doing this have low self-esteem and have to say mean things to you to make themselves feel better. You can just nod your head politely and thank them for the advice. Then walk away believing that their criticism is worthless and has nothing to do with who you are. Do not take it personally, ever. Forgive this person for being in a different place than you are spiritually. Forgiveness is key. Never resent someone for being ignorant. Try to look at everything in a positive light.

Negative categorizing and labeling is similar to criticism and judgment. We all like to categorize and label people and events in our lives as good, bad and neutral. When you do this, you are creating stress in your life. If you can look at events and people in your life as just events and people - and not as good, bad or neutral - it will help alleviate some stress. A few examples of stress causing categorizing are: Seeing a person do something or wear something you don't agree with and immediately placing them in the "weirdo" category. They may be a perfectly nice and smart person, but they did something you didn't like, so you immediately think the worst of them. Another example is when you are driving and someone cuts you off and you immediately say or think "What an idiot driver!"

You can also catch yourself categorizing people by their color, race, nationality or religion. An example of labeling an event is when you go to a party and things don't work out the way you expect, and you say, "That was the worst party in history." You could have just not said or thought anything about it and moved on. Better yet, you could have pointed out the positive things from the party and left the rest alone. The food was tasty, but the people were rude and the music was terrible. Why not focus on the food being good? Every time we put a label on people or events or negatively categorize for any reason at all, we are creating negative energy.

Why can't people just be people and things and events just be things and events? If you want to stay healthy and happy, try to change the way you talk about and think about everything. Start paying attention to your experiences and when you start to put a negative label or category on someone or something, stop yourself and focus on something positive instead. If you cannot find a positive trait, then just drop it all together and move on with your life.

If you have a negative conscious belief about yourself or anything else, you need to write it down on paper, accept it for being a lie, pray or do a visualization to release the belief and come up with a new positive belief or mantra to cancel it out. You may even consider seeing a coach or mental health counselor to help you get rid of the belief. Suppose you have a belief that it's difficult to make money. You would come up with a new belief or mantra that it's easy to make money. Then you would say this to yourself several times a day until the old belief is gone and the new belief becomes a habit.

There are many modalities for reprogramming beliefs including Psych-K, EFT, Emotion Codes, Healing Codes, Hypnotherapy and others. You can web-search these things to find something that resonates with you. When I work with coaching clients, we test muscles and energy to find out which beliefs are a problem for them and then we clear them out with energy work and come up with the replacement beliefs and mantras.

To get rid of unreasonable expectations, you will need to reframe your perception. Expect the unexpected. Anything is possible in this universe. There are unlimited possibilities. When you are expecting something, anything may happen and, in most cases, it's not what you are expecting. One time a lady told me what happened about her image of Italy: she had had such high expectations of what Italy was like and wanted to go there for many years and then when she finally went to Italy, she was completely let down. She said that it was very smoggy, and everyone smoked and she felt that Italy wasn't what she had expected. She told me that if I go to Italy, not to go with any expectations. I have always adopted the belief that I only expect that anything is possible. This principle should be applied to everything.

To reprogram your brain for reasonable expectations, there are a few things you can do. First, you need to work hard to release or let go of any unreasonable expectations you have. It's okay to have some minimal expectation but in many cases you don't need to have any expectation at all. For example, if you go to a restaurant and you have heard glowing reviews of this place, try to put the glowing reviews on the back burner and release any and all expectation of the place other than you expect to have a new experience at a new restaurant. If you do this, if the waiter is having a bad day or the food is not perfect, you will not be disappointed. All sorts of factors and things can happen in life that will take things from being amazing to terrible very quickly. People get sick and then the restaurant can be short of staff. The waiter can be having a bad day, due to recent divorce or a myriad of other issues.

The idea is that if you have no expectation, you have a better chance of being surprised or having a positive outcome. If you have unreasonable expectations, then you will most likely be disappointed.

There are times when you need expectations, but they have to be realistic. For example, if you hire an employee, you cannot expect them to be the perfect super employee who accomplishes the job of three people and is at work and on time every day of the year. In a perfect world, this would be great. However, you can realistically expect that they will get their work done on time, be punctual, do their best job, and show respect and courtesy to you and their fellow employees.

Start paying attention to your expectations and ask yourself "Is this a realistic expectation, or do I have a chance of being let down?" If the answer is that your expectation is unreasonable, then you need to drop it and refocus your mind on something positive.

You can also use manifestation as a way to prevent having to worry yourself with expectations in the first place. If you want to start changing your life so that you do not have negative experiences that will let you down, start saying daily positive mantras or prayers, for example: "I am attracting positive and enjoyable experiences every day" or "All my experiences are enjoyable and happy." When you show up at a restaurant, you will have manifested what you want in your life. I personally use several mantras daily that have made my life much happier and given me positive results everywhere I go, so there is no need for expectation.

Since you are in 100% control of all your thoughts, pay attention to any limiting thoughts or beliefs about yourself and others and get rid of them. Stop telling other people things that limit them and stop having these limiting conversations with yourself. Start believing that you and everyone else around you can accomplish whatever realistic goal they want to co-create with God that is for their highest good.

There are only three things that would prevent you from accomplishing what you want and they are: totally unrealistic goals; the thing you want is not for your highest good; you don't have the physical talent or ability to do it. Unfortunately, our human bodies can sometimes limit us. If you want to be a famous athlete but you have no natural athletic ability and you are uncoordinated, then your goal is unrealistic. There are many things your body can learn to do: you want to lift 100 pounds so you take a weight-lifting class and build up your muscle strength, until you can lift 100 pounds.

When you catch yourself thinking limiting thoughts, stop yourself and cancel the thought out with a mantra or sentence like, "I can do anything that is for my highest good." You can do the same with thoughts about other people. "Bob can do anything that is for his highest good." With some patience and practice, all of the limiting thoughts and beliefs will go away and you will start achieving all your goals and dreams.

Self-Love – Putting Yourself First

You cannot heal yourself emotionally when you don't love yourself 100%. It is important to stop believing the lies you tell yourself in your head and out loud, because they are making you sick. Some of the lies we tell ourselves include things like: "I am not loved"; "Nobody likes me"; "My body is ugly and fat." There is only one truth and that is "You are a child of God and you are perfect in the eyes of God and you are unconditionally loved." Stop telling yourself negative lies about yourself. Whenever you catch yourself doing this, stop yourself and say, "I choose to not believe this lie." Then replace it with something loving, like "I am perfect just the way I am." People who have had some type of abuse or neglect in their lives, have been abandoned by a loved one or people who were raised with unloving family members typically have an issue with self- love. People with low self-esteem for any reason can also use help with self-love. In order to completely love others in a healthy way and manage your stress, you need to master self-love first.

Here are a few tips for practicing self-love:

Putting yourself first: When you respect and take care of yourself before you take care of others, you are practicing a form of self-love. You know how on airplanes, the flight attendant asks you to put the oxygen mask on yourself first before you tend to your child? Well, that is because an adult, with a larger body, will pass out from lack of oxygen first and, if you die, then there will be no one to take care of your child. The same goes for people who neglect their own needs and instead focus only on doing what their boss wants or taking care of others, family and other things.

Self-care needs to be your number one priority. Not only will you be able to live long enough to take care of everyone else, but you will be much better at it also. You cannot be a good doctor, attorney, business leader, mother, teacher or caregiver, if you are falling apart emotionally and physically. In order to be successful in life, you have to be successful within first. Give yourself permission to take care of your body, mind and spirit first and always and you will be practicing the best form of self-love.

Mirror meditation: Look at yourself in the mirror each morning and say to yourself, "(Your Name) I love you unconditionally! You are perfect just the way you are! I love you! I love you! I love you!" Then give yourself a big hug. This may sound silly but if you try this every day for a week, you will start to see a big difference in your selfesteem and in your life. This is an exercise that many psychotherapists and mental health counselors use with their patients. Life coaches like to use it, too. It helps to empower you, building your self-love and self-esteem. Best of all, it will help you to stop tearing yourself apart with lies about yourself when you have conversations in your head.

Night-time mantra/meditation: When you lie down to go to sleep at night, wrap yourself up in your covers and repeat the mantra "I am loved," either in your mind or out loud. It is much more powerful when you say it out loud. You will usually fall asleep while doing this. Try to do it for at least 5 minutes before you fall off to sleep each night. For people who have experienced a lifetime of not feeling loved, this is very powerful, reminding you that in addition to the people who love you, you are also loved unconditionally by God, your angels and guides, ascended masters and all the other beings in heaven who care about you.

Negative speech

In one of the Gospels, there is a story about how Jesus cursed a fig tree and it shriveled up and died. The moral to this story is that your words are more powerful than your thoughts. You can actually make people sick by saying mean, negative or hurtful things to them. Pay attention to your speech and be careful to only speak positive words from your mouth. Quantum physics has proven this story in the Bible by showing that every time you say a negative word or sentence out loud, it carries a negative energy frequency or low vibration that goes out like a ripple in the pond. It harms the person you are speaking to, as well as yourself. If others are listening to it, then it will harm them as well.

Negative speech not only causes you conscious emotional stress and illness but does the same to whomever you use it with. Make sure to pay attention to everything that comes out of your mouth and start reprogramming your mouth for only positive language. When you say positive things to people, it empowers and uplifts them. Also, saying negative things about others behind their backs, is also harmful to you and to the person you are speaking negatively about. The laws of karma kick in whenever you say something negative about anyone. Since we are all connected to one another through the universal energy, the gossip or negative speech about others will come back to you. There are several passages in the Bible that relate to God's opinion of gossip and spreading lies or rumors about others. The bottom line is: If you don't have anything nice to say, don't say anything at all. This was what my mother taught to me and she said it quite frequently.

Attitude and perceptions

Change your attitude and perception to be more positive and you will change your life. You will be much happier and healthier if you take a glass half-full attitude, instead of the glass is always half-empty attitude. Things that you perceive as stressful may not be stressful for others. Everyone has different perceptions, which is why stress affects every human being differently. Something is only stressful if you perceive it that way. Start looking at your problems and the negative events that happen as challenges and learning experiences instead of problems. If you perceive every difficult thing as negative, a threat or you catastrophize things, you will never be happy. Every person in the world has stress but everyone perceives stress differently, which is why each person has a different reaction to stress.

When something you perceive as stressful happens to you, ask yourself, "Do I have control over this?" If the answer is no, then let it go. Put it into a mind balloon and send it up into the sky, or give it over to God. If the answer is yes, then sit down and make a plan with yourself or a relative/friend on how you are going to deal with it.

Start paying attention to how you are perceiving the events, people and situations in your life and put a positive spin on everything. If something is perceived as a threat, then make sure to look at it from a different view and make 100% sure it really is a threat and not an over-reaction. God gave us perception so we can pick out the good from the bad and protect ourselves. However, if you are always perceiving things as a threat, danger or catastrophe, psychologists call this negative forecasting and catastrophizing.

Creating Happiness

Lately, I have heard many people make comments about other people, saying "Susie will never be happy." There are many reasons why some of the people in our lives will never be happy and the main reason is that they have a wrong belief about where happiness comes from in the first place. Earlier, I mentioned having unreasonably high expectations. That is one of the reasons why some people are never happy.

However, there are also some people who have the belief that other people, jobs or material things will make them happy or give them long term happiness. Many people suffer from If Only Syndrome. They run around saying: "If only I had a boyfriend, I would be happy"; "If only I had a higher paying job, I would be happy"; If only I had a Mercedes Benz, I would be happy". My favorite is "If only I had a million dollars, I would be happy." Unfortunately, the key to happiness is not jobs, other people, money, or material things.

According to recent polls, Americans are no happier today than they were 50 years ago despite significant increases in prosperity, decreases in crime, cleaner air, larger living quarters and a better overall quality of life. Happiness is 50 percent genetic, says University of Minnesota researcher David Lykken. According to psychologists, the other 50 percent depends on your determination to be happy. Which may be why Abraham Lincoln once said, "Most people are as happy as they make up their minds to be." I believe that we are 100% in control of our own happiness and we create our own happiness. I also believe that you can get temporary happiness or gratification from things like a new job or money, but you will never receive life-long happiness from those things.

Wouldn't it be nice to be happy every day? Well, the truth is that you can be happy every day, if you choose to be. Happiness is a choice, which is what the wise Abraham Lincoln said.

I recently took a poll on happiness, on my social media accounts to see what my thousands of friends do to be happy. Here are some of the things they said:

Good health
Traveling
Meditating
Spending time with family
Singing and listening to
Playing fun games
Laughing and watching shows that make you laugh
Making other people smile or laugh
Spending time in the outdoors
Volunteering, helping people or doing service for others (seniors, youth, poor and etc)
Living your purpose
Spending time with pets or animals

Playing sports
Camping and Fishing
Doing crafts
Playing musical instruments
Dancing
Building things
Knitting, sewing, crocheting
Bird watching
Hiking

Gardening – Flowers or produce
Reading books, magazines or blogs
Going to church, mosque, temple or synagogue
Time with friends
Meeting new friends
Shopping
Exploring
Visiting museums
Watching butterflies and dragonflies
Collecting fairy statues
Spending time around water (ocean, lake, waterfall)
Looking at antique or classic cars, trucks, motorcycles

These are just a sample of some of the many answers I received when I did my poll on happiness. I am sure you get the idea by now. Happiness comes not only from things but experiences, memories and even spirituality. Happiness comes from going deep within yourself and getting in touch with your higher self, guides and angels. Happiness especially comes with connecting yourself with God and the Universe and seeing your connection to everyone and everything.

If you are someone who is regularly saying, "If only", think very deeply about this. Ask yourself and your Higher Self the question "What do I need to do every day to be happy?" Then, go within yourself, using meditation, quiet time, prayer and reflection and listen to the answers that come up. Write the answers down and start doing what makes you happy every day. You have all the answers within yourself. If you are unhappy right now, here is a new daily mantra for you:

"I am creating my happiness today and every day."

Say this mantra every day of the week, as many times a day as possible, until you see a shift to happiness in your life. Then, start making a conscious choice to be happy. No other person will ever make you happy; only you can do that.

The Healing Power of Forgiveness

When people hurt you and you do not forgive them, the stress from holding onto the hurt and anger will destroy your body, mind and spirit. According to the Eastern practice of Chakra Balancing, un-forgiveness or grudges harm your heart center (chakra) which impacts all of the organs in that region of the body which includes your heart, circulation, lungs and breasts. Other areas of your body that can sometimes be impacted by the emotional stress of un-forgiveness are the stomach, pancreas, liver and gallbladder.

On a metaphysical and energetic level we form what are called Cord Attachments to people who hurt us. Those cords become attached to our heart area and remain there until we cut them away. For some people, it is hard to forgive others and they will hold onto grudges for many years. For others, it's easy to forgive and they just move on.

If you want to heal health issues affecting the "heart center" of the body, you need to forgive everyone from your past who has hurt you and from this moment forward, you need to forgive everyone now and in your future that hurt you. Please keep in mind that forgiving does not mean forgetting. When something bad happens, we need to learn from those lessons and remember the lessons, so we don't repeat mistakes in the future. However, focusing on the incident, thinking about it or speaking about it over and over again will give you more emotional stress. When you forgive someone, you let it go, release it and move forward, but without forgetting the lesson. The best way to forgive someone from your past or present is by telling them either in person, over the phone or in a letter or email that you forgive them.

However, if that is not possible to do for some reason, there are other ways for you to heal your heart center with forgiveness. Here are a few ways you can do this:

Write a letter to that person forgiving them and you can rip it up and throw it away, burn it or bury it in the ground.

Offer up a simple prayer, "Thank you, God, for helping me to forgive _____ for the offense they did to me. Amen." You can make up whatever prayer you want. Say it one or more times a day for a few days until you feel like you have completely forgiven that person.

Do a cord-cutting visualization where you imagine the person who you need to forgive standing in front of you. Visualize the ethereal cord that is attaching your heart to them. Next, visualize Archangel Michael, Jesus or yourself, taking a solid gold sword or giant scissors and cutting the cord. Say the words, "I forgive you <their name>. See the cord transmuting into white light and dust and disappearing. Then imagine the person released and floating away.

Practice Ho'oponopono - This is an ancient practice from Hawaii for forgiveness. According to www.Huna.com, Ho'oponopono means, "To make right." Essentially, it means to make it right with the ancestors, or to make it right with the people you have relationships with. The Huna practitioners in Hawaii believe that the original purpose of Ho'oponopono was to correct the wrongs that had occurred in someone's life including Hala (to miss the thing aimed for, or to err, to disobey) and Hewa (to go overboard or to do something to excess) which were illusions, and even 'Ino (to do harm, implying to do harm to someone with hate in mind), even if accidental.

One warning before proceeding with this practice: Huna practitioners say not to practice this with someone else, without training. When faced with any adverse situation, the Ho'oponopono practitioner will immediately ask "What is it in me that is causing this event to take place, this person to behave this way, this sickness to manifest?" Ho'oponopono practitioners know that blaming others is a sure way for making sure of the recurrence of a problem.

If you cannot get past the habit of blame, I suggest you do not use this meditation and prayer.

The Process of Ho'oponopono:

Bring to mind anyone with has hurt you or with whom you do not feel total alignment or support. In your imagination, construct a small stage below you. Imagine an infinite source of love and healing flowing from a source above the top of your head (from your Higher Self), and open up the top of your head, and let the source of love and healing flow down inside your body, fill up the body, and overflow out your heart to heal up the person on the stage. Be sure it is all right for you to heal the person and that they accept the healing. When the healing is complete, have a discussion with the person and forgive them, and have them forgive you.

Next, let go of the person, and see them floating away. As they do, cut the aka cord that connects the two of you (if appropriate). If you are healing in a current primary relationship, then assimilate the person inside you.

Do this with every person in your life with whom you are incomplete, or not aligned.

The Ho'oponopono prayer that you should use with this exercise:

I love you.
I am sorry.
Please forgive me.
Thank you.

The final test is: can you see the person or think of them without feeling any negative emotions? If you do feel negative emotions when you do, then do the process again.

If you don't like the Ho'oponopono prayer or it doesn't feel comfortable for you, here is a 3-step process that you can try:

Acknowledge that you have been hurt.

Release and forgive the offender.

Get rid of the negative thinking around the event.

Gratitude: Saying Thank You is Not Enough

There have been hundreds of studies done on the positive effects that gratitude has on your body, mind, spirit and even relationships. At the University of Texas Health Science Center, Drs. Blaire and Rita Justice reported, "A growing body of research shows that gratitude is truly amazing in its physical and psychosocial benefits."

In one study on gratitude conducted by Robert A. Emmons at the University of California at Davis and his colleague Mike McCullough at the University of Miami, randomly assigned participants were given one of three tasks. Each week, participants kept a short journal. One group briefly described five things they were grateful for that had occurred in the past week, another five recorded daily hassles from the previous week that displeased them, and the neutral group was asked to list five events or circumstances that affected them, but they were not told whether to focus on the positive or on the negative. Ten weeks later, participants in the gratitude group felt better about their lives as a whole and were a full 25 percent happier than the hassled group. They reported fewer health complaints, and exercised an average of 1.5 hours more.

The plain truth is that if you want to be truly happy in your life, you must have the attitude of gratitude. Saying thank you to people is just a tiny part of gratitude. There is much more to gratitude than that! According to Dr. Robert Emmons, author of Thanks! How Practicing Gratitude Can Make You Happier, there are 3 stages of gratitude: recognizing what we're grateful for, acknowledging it, and appreciating it. The Webster's dictionary defines gratitude as a "feeling of appreciation or thanks." So, we can assume that gratitude is a feeling. However, gratitude is also a practice. They key to success with gratitude is acknowledging the feeling and then practicing activities that show your feeling.

Here is a list of ways that you can start cultivating gratitude and improving your happiness, relationships and life:

Say a prayer at least once a day, explaining what you are grateful for
Taking time throughout the day to notice things you are grateful for
Keep a gratitude journal. At the end of each day before you go to bed, write down all of the things during that day that you feel grateful for. Everything from the blue sky to the dinner you ate works.

When you identify someone or something that is negative, stop yourself and switch it around to a positive trait about the person or thing. Practice a random act of kindness for a stranger. For example paying for the coffee of whoever is standing behind you in the queue at the coffee shop.

Always say "Thank you".

Show your appreciation to a friend or relative by cooking them a meal, giving them flowers or doing some other act of appreciation.
Look for the good in everything, everyone and every situation.
Volunteer your time for a cause.

Donate to charities.
Make a practice to say nice things to people you care about, by regularly pointing out what you appreciate about them.
Show yourself some gratitude and appreciation by doing something nice for yourself.

Pushing the Replay Button on life

How many times in a week do you talk about or think about the past or worry about the future? Whenever you talk about or think about things from your past, the physical, emotional and energetic stress from that process is just as deadly as it was when the event first happened. If I were to strap you to a blood pressure and heart monitor while having you recite a negative event from your past, what you will see is your blood pressure and your heart rate rising. Internally you are dumping stress hormones into your body whenever you think about or talk about negative things from the past.

On an energy level, the negative energy is lowering your vibration and can cause mental and/or physical illness. Stop pushing the replay button! Thinking about it is bad enough, but when you speak about it, the negative energy is much more powerful. When someone harms you, hurts you, or victimizes you, or a bad event happens, you need to clear it out, forgive it, release it and move on. Every time you talk about a story of someone hurting you, or you think about it and bring it up over and over again, you are victimizing and harming yourself over and over again. Forgive the person who harmed you, forgive yourself for allowing it to happen and then move on and don't discuss or think about it anymore. You should only discuss a negative event from your past with someone, when the purpose is to help that person and teach them a lesson you learned from your experience, or you are talking to a therapist. Otherwise, you should never speak of it again.

The best way to train your mind to stop pushing the replay button is by learning how to practice Mindfulness (Present Moment Awareness). You will stop thinking about the past and also stop worrying about the future, if you learn how to be constantly in the present moment. I became a Certified Mindfulness Instructor, because my own practice of

Mindfulness cured me from many years of anxiety, panic attacks and mild depression. I cannot tell you enough about how much the practice of Mindfulness has changed my life, relationships and health for the better

Hitting the Delete Button on Stress

Since you have 100% control over what you allow yourself to perceive as stress and what you allow to create stress in your life, you are fully able to eliminate, change, control or avoid things that you know make you feel stressed. I call this concept, Hitting The Delete Button on Stress.

If you are feeling out of balance or overwhelmed in any way, you have created this for yourself with an overly complicated life.

Here are some examples of why and how you can hit the delete button on stress:

Some people get upset by watching the negative stories on the nightly news. If this is you, then stop watching the news, or record the news with your DVR and fast forward to the weather.

When things like grocery shopping or taking out the trash stress you out, delegate or give them away to another family member.

If checking emails or social media make you feel anxious or stressed, then lump the emails together and check them once or twice a day. Check your social media less often or get rid of social media altogether. My husband never spends time on social media because he hates it; he is happy and keeps in touch with his friends by telephone.

If horror movies make you have nightmares, then don't watch them, even if your friends try to pressure you. Boundaries are really important for hitting the delete button on stress. If someone wants you to do something that is stressful or upsetting to you, then you need the boundaries, courage, self-respect and self-love to tell them No.

If you have a stressful relationship, go get some counseling. Continuing on with the status quo in a stressful relationship will only create health problems and premature death. When you can love yourself enough to get some help, you are moving in the right direction towards your happiness and health.

Completely avoid annoying relatives or others who cause you stress.

You can also get rid of your toxic friendships. If you have friends who are negative energy vampires sucking the life out of you. Get rid of them and move on. You are allowing them to have power over you and make you sick.

I used to have several negative energy vampire friends and as I got emotionally stronger and began fully loving myself, I was able to get them out of my life for good. Now, I only choose to surround myself with friends who are likeminded, kind, loving, supportive, spiritual, grounded and balanced. You are fully entitled to choose who you spend your time with and if you want to be happy you need to spend your time with people who are positive influences in your life.

Hitting the delete button on your stress is easy; you just have to be willing to find the things in your life that create stress and make some changes. No one else will make these changes or deletions for you, it's up to you to love yourself enough to make yourself happy and hit the delete button.

Stuffing Emotions – The Truth Will Set You Free

Many people I know have a problem with talking about their feelings and emotions or sharing their feelings with others. Some people have a problem allowing themselves to experience their emotions and feelings in the first place. They either stuff them down like laundry in a basket, they run away and try to hide from them or they cover up their emotions and pretend everything is okay. Many times you meet people who look happy on the outside but on the inside they are crying inside. One example of this was one of my favorite comedians, Robin Williams. He always acted happy and funny and smiled. On the inside, he was sad and depressed. He was putting on an act so people would think he was okay because he was embarrassed or afraid to let anyone know what was really going on inside. The public finally found out about the demons he wrestled with, after he committed suicide. It was a tragic end for such a talented, brilliant, artistic man. How many people do you know who do this? Maybe you are doing this right now.

When people either stuff, hide, pretend or run away from their emotions it causes mental and physical illness. Society teaches boys from birth that they need to be tough and strong and never show their emotions. I know many men who were raised this way and have a difficult time expressing their feelings. The result is that their relationships are ruined. They wind up divorced and unhappy. They also have a multitude of health problems as a result of the emotional stress that is not being released or dealt with. Since we now know that emotional stress causes up to 98% of illness, don't you think we owe it to ourselves to face our emotions head on and learn to deal with them?

No matter what age you are and what you were told about feelings and emotions by people when you were growing up, it is never too late for you to stop believing the lies and stop the lies from harming you. You have the ability to stop stuffing your emotions. Learn to accept, embrace and claim your emotions and then release them. For example, if you are feeling angry, claim the anger by saying to yourself, I feel mad or angry and accept the fact that you feel that way. You can even tell your spouse, children or whoever that you feel angry right now. It's okay! No one is going to hit you over the head with a baseball bat because you shared your feelings with them.

It is actually the opposite. People want to have healthy relationships and want to know what you are thinking and feeling. They are not going to shun you, hate on you or beat you up, unless they have psychological problems or issues of their own that are causing them to act that way. When you are feeling an emotion, make sure you label the emotions, as excited, angry, confused, sad or frightened. When you claim the emotions, they dissipate and go away. If you stuff them or try to run away from them or deny that you have feelings or emotions, then they will get stronger and make you sick.

Anger, grief, resentment and un-forgiveness (holding grudges) will cause problems with your heart. This is why people tell you to "get it off your chest." Throughout history, people have known that bottling up your emotions causes damage to your heart. Try to release all of your anger, grudges and un-forgiveness. The opposite of anger, hate and un-forgiveness, is love, kindness, compassion and forgiveness. You can heal your heart, by giving love to a pet or relative, being kind and compassionate to others, helping and doing service for others. You also are asked to "get it off your shoulders." That is because when you have emotional stress, it can be like a heavy weight pressing down on your shoulders. Many people – me, too! - tend to carry tension and emotional stress in the neck and shoulders, which become tight and sore.

Have you ever heard: "She is choking down her emotions"? One time, when I was teaching a meditation class at a health club, I had a lady who was coughing and choking during all of the classes. After 3 classes in a row of this lady disrupting our class, I pulled her aside and told her that if she didn't cure her cough, I would have to ask her to leave class until she was no longer coughing. The lady looked tired and unhappy. She continued to tell me about how she had gone to eight doctors and none of them could help her. She had test after test to find out why she was coughing and she was given drugs that didn't work. None of the doctors could ever diagnose and treat her problem. Since I am a Medical Intuitive, I looked at her and I could see that her throat was blocked with emotional upset and that was the cause of her problem.

In the Eastern philosophy of chakras, the throat chakra or throat center has to do with speaking your truth, communicating clearly, and clearly communicating and expressing your emotions and feelings to others. I looked into her eyes and said, "I know exactly what's wrong with you and I can help you. Meet me after the next class." The following week, the lady met with me and I asked her if she had any emotional stress in her life right now. She proceeded to tell me a story about how she wasn't getting along with her daughter and she wasn't able to tell her daughter how she felt. I did some energy healing work and counseling with this lady. I gave her specific instructions for talking with her daughter and telling her how she felt. The lady followed through with my instructions, but I did not see her for a while.

A month or two later, I ran into this lady at the health club and she was glowing and smiling from ear to ear. I asked her about her throat and coughing problem. She exclaimed with great excitement "You healed me!" Then she proceeded to tell me how she followed my directions after the energy work. Her coughing stopped. She hasn't coughed since and her relationship with her daughter has been restored.

Did you ever hear the phrase "what you resist, persists"? If you resist and try to run away from your feelings, they will only get worse. Be willing to accept and acknowledge that you are human, you have feelings that you are entitled to feel and are entitled to express your feelings anytime you want. Start feeling your feelings and stop running away and stuffing them. The reason the Biblical phrase "The truth will set you free" resonates so strongly with people all over the world, is because when you speak your truth to others and tell them how you think or feel about something, it breaks the emotional bonds that cause suffering, stress and illness.

There may be some situations from time to time where you cannot speak your truth because it could harm or damage someone or cause trouble. In that case you should not speak your truth. However, whenever you have a situation where it would be okay to get something off your chest, then love yourself enough to get it all out of your system. Please remember that when you don't share your feelings with people in any relationship, you are sabotaging that relationship. Constant communication is the number one key to relationship success. If you want to work on any of this, consider seeing a mental health practitioner. Start the work on healing your emotional wounds right now, so you can heal your body, mind, spirit and relationships.

Establishing Healthy Boundaries

When I was growing up, I had a mother who was emotionally abusive. She continuously criticized everything I did. My family was very poor and my parents were codependent and emotionally unbalanced. I didn't have much financial security growing up, but I was surrounded by neighborhoods of wealthy families, which were a constant reminder of what I didn't have. I was also bullied in school from preschool until I graduated from high school. As a result of this childhood, I always had low self-esteem. To make matters worse, my parents both had low self-esteem and that didn't help me much. I spent most of my life trying to please everyone, because nothing was ever good enough for the adults in my life. I also have always been a kind, compassionate and loving person, so I am always helping others. I was taken advantage of for years and years because of my childhood and my wanting to please everyone - the carpet that people would walk all over. When my children were younger, I was afraid of being like my mean mother and was too lax with my kids. They needed more discipline, but I could not give it to them because I had poor boundaries. As a result my kids walked all over me like a carpet. I was like a Labrador Retriever Dog, just rolling over at everyone's feet. Does this sound like you or anyone you know?

When you do not have healthy boundaries, you may do one or all of the following things that destroy your life:

You constantly put others first and yourself last.
You attract people into your life who take advantage of you.
You have relationships with toxic people who are making you sick.

You allow yourself to get into and remain in an abusive relationship.
You become exhausted from trying to please everyone.
You have a very hard time saying, "No!" and take on too much work.

You become overwhelmed and overloaded.
You become emotionally stressed.
You create unhappiness.

You cause relationship problems.
You will feel anger, guilt, resentment, blame and shame either with yourself or with all of the people who you let take advantage of you.
You block your ability for success in your life.

Here are some of the major types of boundaries that people have and a few ideas to know if your boundaries are healthy:

Emotional boundaries: When you have healthy emotional boundaries you are able to override your need to please others. You can say No, because when you say Yes too much, you wind up taking on too many things. Your boundaries are healthy when you don't let others push you around, control, criticize or abuse you, smother you, or take advantage of you. Boundaries also have to do with you following through on what you say, for example, disciplining your children. Healthy emotional boundaries can prevent you from giving unwanted advice or receiving unwanted advice. Healthy boundaries keep you from blaming and accepting blame from others.

You also will not over-react to situations. You know your responsibility to yourself and others. When you have healthy emotional boundaries you are able to maintain an invisible line that separates you from others. You are able to separate your emotions from someone else's. Healthy boundaries can protect you from taking other people's comments personal. Healthy boundaries can protect you from feeling guilty for someone else's negative feelings.

Start speaking up for yourself and start speaking your truth!

Mental Boundaries: Your mental boundaries are related to your thinking, beliefs, listening skills, opinions, decision making, values, priorities, ideas, planning, creating and every other non-emotional mental process. You have healthy mental boundaries when you can maintain an opinion, keep others from pushing their beliefs on you, and keep an open mind to new ideas. Healthy boundaries also exist when you are able to listen as much as you speak, make decisions without having to get others to make them for you and have healthy priorities. You have healthy mental boundaries when you can stand up for what you believe in and stand your ground when you make a decision or think that something is right or wrong.

Physical Boundaries: When you are able to maintain your personal space, privacy and protect your body, you have healthy physical boundaries. Physical boundaries also have to do with your willingness to hug or kiss someone or shake their hand. If you protect your physical self by locking doors when you are dressing or going to the bathroom, you have healthy physical boundaries. If someone is playing loud music and it hurts your ears, you have healthy boundaries when you choose to leave the room or ask someone to turn down the music. When someone is smoking, you have healthy physical boundaries when you choose to move to another spot where the air is better. If a department store sales rep wants to spray you with a perfume tester and you say No, you have healthy physical boundaries.

Material boundaries: You have healthy material boundaries when you can give away or lend your material possessions to people in a healthy way. For example, I used to lend my things to friends on a regular basis and would never get them back. I also use to give things away to people because I was always trying to please someone. Because I had boundary issues, I was taken advantage of regularly. When I created healthy boundaries for myself, I stopped lending my possessions out to people except in an emergency situation.

Spiritual and religious boundaries: You create healthy spiritual and religious boundaries when you are able to have your own beliefs and practices without allowing other people to force you to adopt theirs. When people try to shove their religion down your throat or get you to do spiritual or religious practices that you do not believe in or agree with, you are practicing healthy boundaries when you can say, "No, I am not interested in this." You should be able to do your own seeking and research and decide for yourself what you want to believe in without other people forcing their beliefs and practices on you.

Sexual Boundaries: You establish healthy sexual boundaries when you are able to decide when and where you have sex and with whom you have it. You should be able to say No when you don't want to have sex. You should also be able to tell your partner what you want, don't want and what feels good. You need to protect your body from unwanted sexual touch. It is important to learn skills to protect yourself.

Everyone needs to have healthy boundaries in order to have a happy life. In order to have healthy boundaries, you must have what I call The 3 S's: self-esteem, self-respect and selflove. It took me several years to heal my childhood emotional wounds, learn the 3 S's and become an empowered and confident woman. I am so glad I made the effort to empower myself and learn how to have healthy boundaries because now I have healthier relationships and I am happier. If you are someone suffering from low self-esteem, lack of self-respect or lack of self-love, you will need to learn the skills necessary to improve these areas of your life. No one can do this for you, but a life coach or mental health practitioner can help you with the process. You also can read any of the thousands of books written for improving these areas of your life.

Chronic Worry and Anxiety

There are so many people on this planet who are worried about everything from money and career, to health problems, relationships and the future in general. Some people worry about things that are a waste of time and not very important. When I was growing up, I heard people say that when you worry you get gray hair. Now I know why. Worry makes you mentally and physically sick and it is one of the largest causes of emotional stress. Worry leads to anxiety disorders and many other problems. I know people who have developed nasty stomach ulcers from worrying all of the time.

According to the science of Energy Medicine and the ancient study of the Chakras, worry and anxiety is stored in your Solar Plexus, which is your confidence power house and located between your rib cage and belly button. The negative energy from worry impacts all of the organs in the solar plexus area, mainly the stomach, gallbladder, liver, pancreas and large intestine. A digestive problem is one of the many signs that you suffer from worry and anxiety. There are also many other health problems you may get from the negative energy associated with chronic worry and anxiety, because it impacts every cell and system of the body. Another place besides the stomach that people can really feel their anxiety is in their muscles, particularly the neck and shoulder muscles. I know tons of people who carry their worries and anxiety in their neck and shoulders.

Every person has a different level of worry and anxiety in their life. There are some people who have never been anxious and only have a few worries from time to time. My husband has never been anxious in the 30 years I have known him and he only worries about very important things, and from time to time. Recently, he has experienced legitimate worry about our teenagers getting good grades so they can go to college. However, I have had clients come to me with the other extreme: the people who worry so much that they are sick all of the time and have panic attacks.

That was me many years ago before I healed myself. Shortly after having my children, I was diagnosed with Generalized Anxiety Disorder (GAD), which is the most common type of anxiety disorder and is basically chronic worry about everything, every day for a long period of time. GAD is becoming a common condition these days in this stress-filled, fast paced, high-pressure society we live in. In my situation I had been raised by negative, worry wort parents so I had a predisposition for this problem. Starting when I was pregnant with my oldest child, I developed bad health problems. The health problems got worse during my second pregnancy and I almost died in childbirth.

My health issues continued on after the kids were born. The different doctors I saw were not able to help me with my health problems and I was very scared and worried. I got extremely anxious about all of my health problems. When you combine the health problems with my being a new mom - babies don't come with instruction manuals - with no family support, having left an extremely satisfying and successful career to raise kids, GAD was the logical outcome. Back in those days, I didn't understand about stress, how to deal with it and what it does to you.

Besides GAD, there are other types of anxiety disorders including:

Panic Disorder - When you have feelings of terror that happen for no reason and with no warning and they are accompanied by symptoms like sweating, chest pain, heart palpitations, feeling like you are going crazy, feeling a lump in your throat or a choking sensation.

Social Anxiety disorder – This is where you are overwhelmed with worry and selfconsciousness in social situations like parties, the mall, a theatre event, a wedding, an airport and etc. Sometimes the worry is caused by a fear of being judged by others or getting embarrassed somehow. You may be afraid to go to these events because you feel so uncomfortable in these social situations. Some people feel uncomfortable being in crowded situations and in close proximity to strangers.

Phobias – A phobia is an intense fear of a specific object or situation, such as snakes, heights, or flying. The level of fear is usually inappropriate to the situation and may cause the person to avoid common, everyday situations.

Generalized anxiety disorder: This disorder involves excessive, unrealistic worry and tension, even if there is little or nothing to provoke the anxiety.

According to an article in Health Magazine and www.health.com, there are 12 signs that you have an anxiety disorder:

Excessive worry
Sleep problems
Muscle tension

Irrational fears
Digestive problems or chronic indigestion
Self-consciousness

Stage fright
Panic or panic attacks
Flashbacks

Perfectionism
Compulsive behaviors
Self-doubt

There are many things that cause anxiety and worry. The exact cause of anxiety disorders is unknown, but some scientific research suggests that anxiety disorders are caused by a combination of factors, including changes in the brain and environmental stress. Like other brain illnesses, anxiety disorders may be caused by problems in the functioning of brain circuits that regulate fear and other emotions. A few studies have shown that severe or long-lasting stress can change the way nerve cells within these circuits transmit information from one region of the brain to another. In some other studies, they found that people with certain anxiety disorders have changes in certain brain structures that control memories linked with strong emotions. Some of these studies have shown that anxiety runs in families and may be partially inherited. Since my mother and several people in her family had anxiety and depression, I am not surprised that I wound up being anxious as well. There is also scientific evidence that certain environmental factors like a traumatic event might trigger anxiety in people who have inherited the tendency for developing it.

For many people, worrying and anxiety stems from "What if" thinking. We all are subject to death, job loss and other potential disasters. When people focus on and ruminate on these types of thoughts, anxiety arises and eventually an anxiety disorder manifests. That is exactly what I used to do back in the day when I was stressed out and didn't know what to do. I would constantly think to myself and sometimes say out loud, "What if this happens and what if that happens?"

Now that you have a good picture of what worry and anxiety is all about, let's talk about a few things you can do now to get rid of worry and anxiety:

Practice Mindfulness. Mindfulness is present moment awareness or insight. It's a daily practice that can also be used as a meditation. When you have worries, you are pulled out of the present moment and concentrate on what might happen. The anxiety you create from this can have a negative impact on your decision-making and so much more. Mindfulness involves focusing all of your thoughts on what you are doing right now in this moment. The idea is that when you are constantly present and in the moment, it's very difficult to worry about the future, lament about the past or do "What if?" thinking.

There are many books, videos and CD's on how to practice Mindfulness. I have included my two favorite in my book list at the end of this chapter. A quick example of mindfulness is "Eating an apple".

You focus in on the color of the apple, the smell of the apple, the taste, juiciness and crunch. When a thought, event or person pulls your attention off the apple, you mindfully note it and return to focusing on that apple again. Eventually after practicing this day after day, the worry thoughts and anxiety just go away.

Learn how to practice deep breathing and relaxation techniques so you can use them whenever you are thinking worry thoughts or feeling anxious. You can actually shut down a panic attack before it gets going by doing special breathing. I have had several clients with panic disorder come to me for help and I teach them several breathing exercises that can either help them get through the attacks, stop the attacks or prevent them. The breathing is like a disconnect button on the panic attack. You would also use the techniques the minute you catch yourself thinking a worry thought to defuse it.

Start paying attention to your worry thoughts, label them as worry thoughts and notice if they are really worth worrying over. Many people worry over insignificant things that are not important. What happens with the worry thoughts is that you sometimes fall down a rabbit hole of worrying where you think of one worry thought, which leads to another and another and another. Before you know it, you have been worrying for several minutes. Part of the practice of mindfulness is paying attention to your thoughts: noticing and labeling the thought and then letting it go and returning to focusing on the present moment.

Positive thought replacement to reprogram your brain. After you catch yourself thinking a worry thought, immediately cancel it out with the positive opposite. "My kids might get hurt" would be replaced with "My kids are always safe and protected." You can also use a small prayer as your positive thought replacement.

Turn your "What if" thoughts around. Do a 360 on your "What if" thoughts, by changing them to the positive opposite. "What if my wound festers and I die?" would change to "What if my wound heals quickly and I am back to work in 2 days"? The idea is to catch yourself each time you catastrophize, and add something positive afterwards. Remember that you create with your thoughts, so you always want to focus your thoughts on positive things. If you continue to pay attention and catch yourself each time, eventually you can override all of your stinking thinking in place of positive thinking.

Accept and observe all your thoughts and feelings. Start looking at your thoughts from an outsider or scientist perspective. Study your thoughts like they are in a lab and you are the scientist. This is a part of the practice of mindfulness. You will begin viewing these thoughts as separate from yourself. You need to separate your thoughts from reality and recognize that they are not actual events, they are just thoughts with no form. Don't try to rid yourself of your thoughts, just learn how to look at them from another point of view that is not so negative.

Read books about managing anxiety, worry and panic. If you practice a particular religion - anything from Buddhism and Hinduism to Judaism, Islam and Christianity - there are passages in every holy book that pertain to the topics of worry, anxiety and panic. You will need to look them up or consult your religious advisor. The religious book that helped me with my own anxiety and worry is the Bible. There are many passages that pertain to these subjects, however my favorite passage is this one:

Philippians 4:6-7 (NLT)
Don't worry about anything. Instead pray about everything. Tell God what you need and thank him for all that he has done. If you do this you will experience God's peace, which is far more wonderful than the

human mind can understand. His peace will guard your heart and minds as you live in Christ Jesus.

There are foods and beverages that will increase your anxiety and worry and also chemicals in foods that change your brain chemistry. Be really careful what you eat and drink if you suffer from worry, anxiety or panic disorders. Caffeine, sugar, red and other color food dyes and stimulants of any kind, will all increase your problems. If you are a coffee drinker, you will have to switch for a different beverage if you want to remain calm. Coffee causes even non-anxious people to feel nervous and jumpy. If you are already anxious, you will feel even worse after drinking caffeine or drinking any beverage or food that acts as a stimulant.

Consider trying calming foods and drinks like oatmeal, bananas, chamomile tea, lemon balm and etc. You can drink decaffeinated coffees and teas. If you need the energy jolt that caffeine brings you to do your job, you can try B complex vitamins which give you natural energy without the side effects. Cutting carbs and eating small frequent meals throughout the day will give you continuous sustained energy. The drop in energy is usually caused by blood sugar changes throughout the day, so eating 5 small meals a day, or 3 meals with healthy snacks in between, keeps your blood sugar from dropping or spiking and helps sustain your energy.

Take and use herbs, supplements, and remedies when you feel anxious or have a panic attack. When I suffered from anxiety, I spent many days and hours researching what to do and take for it. I personally tried tons of supplements and herbs out, until I could find some that worked for me.

I would like to share with you here, my own personal list of things that have worked well for me in the past and that I still use daily. I also recommend these to my clients. If you want to know about all of the other hundreds of supplements on the market that are beneficial for anxiety or panic, you will need to do a little research. Please proceed with caution when using anything you have not taken before. Check with your doctor and or pharmacist to make sure it is okay for you to use these things, especially if you are taking any RX medications. Also research these to find out how much to take and how often before you start. Please remember that every person's body is different, needs different amounts and can have different results.

I recommend starting out with tiny amounts and working your way up. Consult your doctor first!

Magnesium Citrate or Magnesium Gluconate. It is usually recommended to take between 350 and 500 MG daily, split up in divided doses during the day.
Glycine powder
B Complex vitamins. For many people this will calm you down, but for some people it can make you more nervous so proceed with caution.

Lemon Balm (Melissa)
Passion Flower - Chamomile tea
Lavender

Bach Flower Remedies. You will need to see a Bach Flower Remedy practitioner to get a custom remedy for you, or you can research and just buy them for yourself.
Homeopathic remedies. You need to see a Homeopathic doctor for these

Use Aromatherapy to remain peaceful and calm. There are many ways to use aromatherapy, from candles and diffusers to putting oil directly on your body. I love aromatherapy and try to use it every day, in my home and on my body. You can use aromatherapy to energize or to calm, so make sure that when you are anxious you are using the calming oils, not the invigorating ones. The following oils are known for creating a sense of peace and calming. My favorites are lavender, cedar, Roman chamomile, jasmine, Melissa and lemon.

Lavender essential oil (anti-anxiety)
Cedar (calming)
Roman Chamomile

Geranium essential oil (balancing)
Mandarin essential oil (calming)
Bergamot essential oil (relaxing)

Ylang Ylang essential oil (sedative)
Neroli essential oil (anti-depressant)
Jasmine essential oil (sedative)

Lemon essential oil (tonic)
Melissa essential oil (balancing, induces confidence) - Palmarosa essential oil (calming to the mind)

Patchouli essential oil (helps with stress-related issues) - Petitgrain essential oil (nerve tonic)
Sandalwood essential oil (sedative)

You Have Nothing to Fear, Except Fear Itself

Fear is a natural response to perceived emotional or physical danger. Fear also causes a huge release of cortisol and adrenaline into the body whenever we have a fearful thought, feeling or perception. Most people will experience some type of body symptom as a result of fear including racing heart, sweating, rise in blood pressure, tight feeling in chest, queasy feeling in stomach and skin tingling. In fact, the anxious feelings we get when we are afraid are a standardized biological reaction, according to medical experts. The body reacts to fear the same way no matter what it is you are afraid of.

Fear is very important for humans to have, because without it we could not protect ourselves from legitimate threats. There are basically good fears and bad fears. Good fears would be feeling fearful when someone points a gun in your direction or when you have to cross a busy road. A bad fear would be something like fear of heights or fear of eating red vegetables. The bad fears are known as false fears, which is why you hear the saying, "FEAR = False Evidence Appearing Real."

Many of these false fears we have are a learned reflex and can be the result of traumas or bad experiences. Some of our false fears were put into our heads by other people, like our parents or friends. I have always heard stories from people that their mother told them to be afraid of some person, place or thing and then they embraced that fear for their entire life. Some fears can even arise from hearing stories of other people's bad experiences. For example, my mother told me a story when I was a child, that my great grandfather was kicked in the head by a horse and died. After I heard that story, I had a lifelong fear of being near horses because I was worried about getting kicked in the head. Sometimes we can adopt other people's fears as our own; if your husband is afraid of driving on a certain highway, you can unconsciously take that on as your belief as well.

In Psychology Today Karl Albrecht Ph.D. identified 5 basic types of fear that all other types of fear stem from:

Extinction: When you fear annihilation or fear that you will no longer exist. You can also call it fear of death. I had this problem for many years, until I had several near death experiences and learned that, when I die, I get to go to another place that is much better. If you are afraid of heights, hang-gliding, or eating bad mushrooms, it's really a fear of death.

Mutilation: When you have a fear of losing or harming any part of your body, internally or externally.

Loss of Autonomy: When you fear being immobilized, paralyzed, restricted, enveloped, overwhelmed, entrapped, imprisoned, smothered, or otherwise controlled by circumstances beyond your control. This is a form of Claustrophobia.

Separation: When you have fear of abandonment, rejection, loss of connectedness, fear of not being wanted, respected, or valued by anyone else.

Ego-death: When you fear humiliation, shame, or any other mechanism of selfdisapproval that threatens the loss of integrity of the Self. The fear of being unloved, unworthy or incapable. When you fear business failure or you fear losing your job, it fits into this category.

Since we have already discussed throughout this book that negative thoughts like fears, harm your body, mind and spirit and make you sick, you need to work hard to get rid of the false fears that are not important to your survival. Learn how to confront and eliminate your false fears, since it's one of the biggest causes of emotional stress.

First, you will need to pay attention to your thoughts and words throughout the week and notice when you are having a fear that is not a legitimate survival fear. If you have false fears, write them down on a paper so you can create a plan to eliminate them. There are many things you can do to get rid of false fears. Some of the techniques that are helpful for dealing with fears include affirmations, counseling, Hypnotherapy, spiritual practice, reading religious books and using emotional healing techniques.

For some fears, it's best to face them head on. If you have a fear of public speaking you can face your fears by speaking over and over again. Over time, it gets easier and easier and the fear goes away. You can use this tactic with driving on the freeway and many other things. You can learn to reprogram your mind by using thought cancellation and positive affirmations. Some people say that inside the Bible, there is one passage for every day of the year that tells you not to fear.

I haven't personally counted them all to confirm that number, but there certainly are a lot of passages telling you not to fear. The message is very clear that we are not supposed to have false fears. If we believe we are safe and protected, then we are safe and protected. What you believe is what you receive. We create that protection with our own thoughts and minds and we also co-create it with God.

Here is my favorite affirmation for getting rid of false fears. When you say this affirmation to yourself throughout the day, make sure to believe it and picture in your mind a host of angels and God surrounding and protecting you always.

"I am always safe and protected"

Emotional Healing the Jesus and Buddha Way

What do the Buddha, Jesus Christ, Saint Germain and all Ascended Masters who have ever walked the earth have in common? They all taught the same major concepts of spreading love, kindness, compassion and forgiveness to everyone. There is even a book that was written called Jesus and Buddha – The Parallel Sayings because their teachings were so similar. If you look at all of the major religious books throughout time from the Buddhist sutras, the Holy Bible and the Tao Te Ching, to the I Am Discourses, you will see that they are all spreading the same truths of practicing love, kindness, compassion and forgiveness. There are also many other teachings that these masters and books have in common.

Even many self-improvement teachers, like Dr. Wayne Dyer, spread these same concepts. When I saw Dr. Dyer speak in Seattle in November, 2012, the main idea I took away from his speech was "I need to be unconditional love." He spoke the same message that all the great masters have taught throughout history. We know that our thoughts, words and actions create our life with either positive or negative energy and we attract to ourselves that which we put out into the world. When you spread love, kindness, compassion and forgiveness you are putting that positive energy in motion and creating a universal boomerang of positive things that can flow back to you. If you want to receive these expressions from others, you must first practice them and give them to yourself. It all starts with you. [Keep in mind that even if you are the kindest person in the world, some sad events can still come to you via divine mandate. There are some things we go through that are just part of our journey of learning.]

Every human on earth has the same want and need which is happiness and love and this is the best way to achieve that. You have to give these virtues to yourself first and then spread them to others. If you are unable to be loving, kind, compassionate and forgiving to yourself or to others, you will always be unhappy and emotionally stressed. You also cannot expect to receive any of these things back, if you are unwilling or unable to give them out. To me the key to my own happiness is being able to give and receive love, kindness, compassion and forgiveness. In fact, I know that my purpose and mission on this earth is to be a spiritual teacher and healer and to spread love, kindness, compassion and forgiveness to as many people as I possibly can before I leave this life.

Letting Go of Control

There are times when it's important to be in control of your body, mind and circumstances. However, there are also times when you don't have control over a situation or when controlling a situation will cause problems in your life. There are many people who are addicted to control (control freaks). Some people can have the opposite problem and have no self-control. It is extremely unhealthy to control other people or have a need to constantly be in control of everything. It is unhealthy to have total loss of control and it's also unhealthy to allow other people to have control over you. Loss of control is typical for people who have addiction problems. People who allow others to control them, typically have a history of abuse or they may have very low self-esteem and lack of boundaries.

Don't be a control freak. Learn the act of allowing. Things are not supposed to always go the way you want them to, so why waste your energy? Just allow things to happen in your life the way they are supposed to, and don't try to control everything. There are some things that you have control over and should have control over, like your behavior, the job you do at work and other things. The things that you should not be controlling, you need to let them go.

Another thing that many people do, a classic control issue, is being deeply attached to the outcome of things. For example, you apply for a job and then you bet the whole farm on whether or not you get hired for this job. When you don't get the job, you get emotionally upset because you were too dependent on the outcome of that situation. Whenever you do anything, start trusting that the outcome will be for your highest good. You can pray and ask for an outcome, believe it will happen, but release it and let it go without attachment to the outcome.

This is part of the Law of Attraction program that has been around for many years.

One exercise that I look to use with my clients is to picture the person, situation, event or problem in your mind and then visualize that you put it into a bubble and it floats up, up and away into the sky. You can also just say a prayer and ask God to take the situation out of your hands. If you continue to have control issues and especially when family, friends or others have noticed or commented that your controlling behavior is impacting your relationships or your job, you should consider going to a therapist.

Let go and let God.

Stop and Smell the Coffee

In Chapter 1 of this book, I talked about how we live in a fast-paced society that is aiding in the worldwide stress epidemic. Everyone who lives in these times is used to instant gratification. You walk into a store and buy whatever you want right now at this moment. You don't have to wait for things to be made by hand for hours and days because we have such an instant society. People who are alive today would never survive on the prairie or during historical times when everything was slow, handmade by humans and there were no computers, cell phones or electricity.

The problem with having all of the technology we have today is it adds a whole new layer of stress into everyone's lives. You have to constantly be tied to your cell phone and you are available for people to hunt you down wherever you go. People rarely get to experience privacy, peace or quiet time because there are always phones ringing, emails coming in, machines going, loud noises everywhere, transportation speeding by and etc. Everyone is always in a hurry to get somewhere. This global lifestyle is stressing us all out.

When I was in college, I took a class called Sociology of the Family. In that class we watched a documentary film about a village in the mountains of Mexico, where people all lived way past 100 years old. They interviewed all of the people in this village and tried to find out why people in this village lives so much longer than in other places. The oldest man in the village was 135 years old and had a wife who was 89. She was his 4th wife. He said that he walked barefoot from his farm for 10 miles into the village every day. There were no cars or telephones allowed in this village, with the exception of a delivery truck once in a while. The people walked everywhere or used donkeys and carts. There were no paved roads in the village either. The people gathered in the square daily and socialized. Everyone lived in little huts and on farms. They all lived very simple lives. They did not have computers, electronics, manufacturing facilities or anything that we have in our modern world. They had a little farmers market where people could get their produce and eggs every day and they had a butcher shop and a bakery for bread. Everything was made by hand in this village. They had a small Catholic church in their village and everyone in the area attended it every week. Basically, these people were living similar to how the pioneers lived in the 1500's.

The 135 year old man said that he believed one of the keys to his longevity was that he was happy every day and he was still having sex with his wife. What the scientists who made this documentary and studied these people concluded, is that their long lives were attributed mainly to: a slower paced lifestyle; lack of stress; social connection; daily physical exercise from manual labor and walking; eating a basic all natural, farm raised diet; having regular sex even past age 100 and all of the villagers were happy. This story obviously tells us that if we slow down our pace and take time for family, friends, exercise and sex we will have less stress and live longer. Perhaps when we unplug and remove all of the electronics and other things that keep our minds going, and instead make up our minds to be happy, we will have a longer and more stress free life.

Everyone I meet complains about how fast their time is going by. If they would slow down the pace of their life, this would not be a problem. When someone who you care about passes away and you realize that you didn't spend enough time with them, that's when you start thinking that it's time to stop and smell the coffee. Why wait until someone dies, when you can start slowing the pace down now?

Here are 10 tips for you to slow down your life and live more stress free:

Don't be in a hurry all of the time to go places. Stop rushing around and causing yourself stress. Plan padding time around your appointments so you are not rushing around. Learn some time management skills.

Don't try to do everything at once, instead try taking baby steps in your life and slowing yourself down.

Unplug regularly by turning off your cell phone unless you are expecting an urgent or important call. Make sure to especially unplug when you are on vacation. It is not really a vacation if you are attached to electronics 24/7.

Don't be so attached to your electronic devices. You don't have to take your laptop and notepad and hand held video game player everywhere you go.

Spend your lunch times at a park watching the ducks, reading a book or sitting in the sun in your back yard. Just do something relaxing, where you can quiet your mind.

Get together with friends and family regularly. Remember that when they are gone you will regret that time not spent together. Make it a point to pencil your loved ones into your schedule.

Create healthy work-life balance.

Do something for yourself, every day that makes you feel happy. Your time is short on earth and you need to take care of yourself. Put yourself first on your to-do list.

Be adventurous and try new things. Go to a new restaurant and try a new food. Go to new bar with your friends. Go take a scuba diving lesson. Go jump on a trampoline with your kids.

Practice Mindfulness or meditation. Stay in the present moment.

Healthy Relationships Begin With You

Relationship stress always ranks in the top 5 of every stress study ever done. Most people have at least one or more difficult relationships in their life, whether it's with a family member, co-worker, friend or neighbor. It's impossible to get along with every person since we all have our own unique personalities, beliefs, opinions, values, faults, intelligence and glitches. Don't forget free will, which allows us to make choices, including poor choices. Humans are not perfect. We are all a work in progress.

When you are in any difficult relationship, there are only two things you can do: change yourself or get out of that relationship. Having a healthy relationship with all of the people in your life, begins with you, since you will never be able to change others, unless they want to change. You can work on yourself (change yourself) and you can protect yourself. If you want to be healthy and happy, it's important to work on having healthy relationships. Unhealthy relationships are one of the biggest causes of emotional stress.

When I am coaching a client, who is married or in a serious live-in relationship, I like to work with both members of the couple. People who are in a close intimate relationship, who spend a large amount of time together and sleep in the same bed, can become emotionally bonded and empathic each other. This means they pick up all of their partner's problems. When your partner feels sick, tired or emotionally upset in any way, it can impact you emotionally, physically and energetically. When they cannot sleep, you may not be able to sleep. When they are upset or angry, you may feel on edge. My husband and I have been together for 30 years and he is like my other half. Any time he is not feeling well emotionally or physically it impacts me. When he doesn't feel well and cannot sleep, I pick that up and cannot sleep. We have even experimented with him sleeping in another room when he has a cold. When he is unable to sleep, I cannot sleep despite him being in another room. That is because of our close bond to one another.

Sometimes this type of empathy can also happen with parents and children. I personally have experienced this with my own mother when I was growing up and now I experience it with my own daughter. What I found out years ago, when I started coaching married client, is that I would teach my client stress management skills and then they would go home to someone who didn't have those skills. Even though they personally felt happier and healthier, they would have setbacks when their spouse was having issues. They would feel bad whenever their spouse felt bad. The skills they were using on themselves did not protect them from the energetic and empathic bond they had with their spouse. After that realization, I started coaching couples together and found that they had much better results and a higher level of happiness in their lives. From time to time I have married clients whose spouses will not accept coaching, so I only work on the one partner. My client still receives positive results and improvements in their life, but the results are not as good as they could be when both partners receive coaching. This is one of the many reasons why marriage counseling with both partners is really good for any person having trouble in their marriage.

Despite the empathy you may have with a partner, relationship success still begins with you and changing yourself first. Your relationships with other people in your life, including at work, needs to start with working on you.
Here are 21 ways you can improve your relationships:

Always be your authentic self and speak your truth. If you are angry or upset with someone, tell them how you feel. Don't stuff, hide and run away from your emotions. Your relationship will never get better by doing this. You have to be honest with people if you want happy relationships.

Make sure to have constant, open and positive communication with your spouse, boss, family, friends and other people who are important in your life. I believe the reason why my husband and I have been together for 30 years, is because we constantly communicate with one another. When communication breaks down, relationships fail, whether it's a business relationship, work relationship, friendship or marriage.

Try to always focus on the positive aspects of the other person. Don't focus in on their faults and bad aspects. Whenever you point out something negative to someone, make sure to have at least 3 positive compliments you can give them first. Constantly pointing out the negative without any positive will ruin any relationship.

Do not be critical or judgmental. I said earlier in this book that every time you criticize or judge you are pulling away from God. Every person is an extension of you and connected to you. Try to focus on you and let other people find their path. You are not in charge of other people's journeys. They are in charge of their journey.

When you have a problem with a person, try to work together with that person to find a solution. When you and another person have a common problem, sit down with that person and find a solution. Make a plan for how you will solve the problems. (Example: You and your spouse have financial problems and you work together on a money plan.) Don't worry or get angry about the problem because worry and anger will only make you sick and not solve your problem. Putting on your thinking cap solves problems.

Look at each relationship challenge as an opportunity to strengthen your relationship.

Don't blame the other person. Blaming only makes people angry and ruins relationships. Nothing good ever comes from blame. If there is a problem, bring it to the other person's attention and work on solving it, without blaming anyone for the problem.

Listen to the other person and always acknowledge them. Always respond to their concerns. Everyone has a need to be heard and acknowledged. This is a natural and normal ego need that every person has on this planet. You want others to hear you and acknowledge you so make sure you do the same for others.

If someone makes you angry, either take a deep breath and a minute to compose yourself before you respond in a calm manner, or walk away until you cool down and then respond when you are calm. An angry or hate filled response will always create a fight or a problem and ruin your relationships. Do not react to negative news or a negative comment; respond in a dignified, civilized manner.

Honor other people's feelings. Every person is entitled to their own feelings and so are you. When someone expresses their feelings to you, never minimize, discount, judge, criticize or condemn their feelings. Always validate and acknowledge others' feelings and respond in a positive manner. Make sure that you express your own feelings as well.

Treat every human and animal with respect and consideration. If you want to receive respect, you must be willing to give it out first.

Be an encourager. Try to be supportive, uplifting and encouraging to your spouse, family, friends and other people in your life. When you put positive energy out to other people, you will receive back positive energy from others. Mutual encouragement is a great anti-stress tool.

Frequently tell your spouse and other family members that you love them. Make sure to remind your spouse how important they are to you. Frequently point out to the people in your life why you like them or why they are special.

Do random acts of kindness for your spouse, family, friends, bosses, co-workers and others in your life. You could make breakfast for your spouse, buy your boss breakfast, or mow your neighbor's lawn.

Be loving, kind, compassionate and forgiving to every person you meet.

Put yourself in the other person's shoes. When someone has a beef with you, try to look at it from their viewpoint. Maybe their concern is valid, but you will not know that if you are only coming from a point of ego or respond to feeling attacked. You cannot improve yourself if you are not willing to listen to other people's issues with you.

Be willing to compromise. Someone told me years ago that the secret to all relationship success was willingness to compromise. No one is going to think just like you, believe the same way you do and have the same opinions as you, so you have to be willing to meet people in the middle.

Be flexible and willing to adapt to other people. Don't take the "It's my way or the highway" approach or you will ruin all of your relationships. Be willing to constantly improve yourself by reading relationship books, taking classes or listening to relationship CD's. There is always room for improvement.

Do not stay in an abusive or destructive relationship with someone who is not willing to change or improve. This is a recipe for illness, disaster and possible death. You are endangering your life every day that you stay in a destructive relationship.

If you need relationship help, see a counselor, coach or religious adviser.

Subconscious Emotional Stress

While conscious emotional stress is the top-of-the-mind stuff that you know about and have complete control over, subconscious stress is buried in your subconscious. Researchers say that 95% of our thoughts come from the subconscious mind and only 5% come from the conscious mind. You don't know the thoughts are there and you cannot control them, like you can conscious thoughts. According to various books, websites, scientific studies and doctors, subconscious emotional stress can keep someone from losing weight, cause and increase pain in your body, cause mental health problems and create many physical health problems and illnesses. Subconscious emotional stress works like a tape recording playing over and over again in the background of your mind. Subconscious emotional stress forms when information goes into your brain, starting from the moment you are in the womb. The information is put there by your experiences, parents, other family members, neighbors, friends, teachers, strangers, media, television, books, movies and other people and things. You hear the information, read it, watch it or experience it and then you forget about what happened. You need your subconscious mind to recall your childhood and past. Our habits, personality, character traits, beliefs and learned behaviors are all registered in the subconscious mind. Your conscious mind generates thoughts and decides what to do, and your subconscious mind carries out the instructions.

The subconscious mind is affected by stress from the minute you are conceived. I never realized how true this was until I attended a Hay House event where Dr. Lipton talked about emotional and cellular stress, including a video of a married couple fighting while the mother was pregnant.   There was a baby monitor/ultrasound and they videotaped the reactions while this couple was fighting. The poor little fetus was jumping around and freaking out in the womb from all the yelling and screaming going on by the mother. When a pregnant mother is stressed, her heart rate and blood pressure go up, she releases cortisol, adrenaline and lots of negative energy that harm the baby. I remember distinctly that when I watched this video, I gasped in horror along with everyone else in the audience. If you are pregnant, the baby is being made physically sick every time you are stressed out. Any sounds and words that are heard prior to birth, can go into their subconscious and scar them for life.

The cells in your body have not forgotten about this subconscious stress, because according to Dr. Lipton in Biology of Belief, all of the conscious and subconscious emotional stress, negative experiences and information is recorded by and absorbed by every cell in your body. Stress goes into every cell in your body and stays in your cells forever, causing current and/or future health problems in your mind and body. The only way to clear your cells and body of stress is through a special healing modality like Psych K, Emotion Codes, Healing Codes, Body Talk, Chakra Healing or other energy healing modalities. You have to use a healing modality to get rid of the stress or the stress will cause illness in your body and mind.

That is why it is so important to read this book and many others and learn how to prevent stress. Besides using modalities to clear stress out of your cells, you can reprogram your subconscious mind by inputting and reinforcing new positive thoughts, positive ideas and positive actions. Here are some of the many ways you can reprogram your subconscious mind to over-ride negative information and stress:

Positive Affirmations and positive self-talk
Hypnotherapy

EMDR (Eye movement desensitization and reprocessing) is a primary therapy treatment for trauma. EMDR is highly recommended by Dr. Lipton for healing subconscious emotional stress.

Visualizations, which involve closing your eyes and seeing information or movies that you create on your mind screen.
Meditation
Subliminal Audios/Videos

Auto-Suggestion (Self-Suggestion). An example of this would be that you want to remember to take out the trash tomorrow morning, so before you go to bed, you say to yourself, "I want to take out the trash at 8:00 AM so tomorrow morning you will get up and take out the trash at 8:00 AM, no matter what."
Essential Oils

PSYCH-K®, to free oneself from limiting sub-conscious beliefs
NET (Neuro-Emotional Technique) for finding and removing neurological imbalances in the body-mind

BODYTALK SYSTEM, for improving communication between the body/mind to improve health at all levels
BACH FLOWER ESSENCES, a system of flower remedies that corrects emotional imbalances

EFT (Emotional Freedom Technique)
Emotion Codes

The Silva Mind Method
Subconscious Ascension
Theta Clearing

You will have to research each of these methods to find out which ones you want to try out and what resonates with you. Your subconscious mind can have limiting beliefs or wrong beliefs that you have acquired since birth and those wrong or limiting beliefs will block your ability to manifest what you want and block your ability to improve your life and heal your body. What I found out from healing myself is that most of the illnesses and health problems I had were caused by subconscious limiting beliefs that were impacting my health. That explained why I went to doctors and healers who could not help me. Once I was able to identify the subconscious issues, I was finally able to heal myself from many different problems. Almost all of the stressful things I discussed in the previous section on Conscious Emotional Stress, also affect your subconscious mind.

If you want to find out what the beliefs, ideas, limits and other subconscious stressors you have, you can use the techniques I list here to do so. You can also use a few other techniques that are specific to diagnosing what the subconscious issue is. Here are a list of what I use on myself regularly. These techniques have helped me to figure out many problems and bring them up to the surface for clearing out.

Kinesiology or Muscle Testing -
Mindfulness or Insight Meditation. You can go within yourself to ask your Higher Self questions to find out what needs healing.
Using a Pendulum
Chakra energy scan
Reiki

You will notice that this section is much shorter than my section on conscious emotional stress and that is because you are in full control of your conscious mind, so there is so much more to talk about and learn. You are limited with the subconscious. Because 95% of your thoughts come from the subconscious mind, it's important that you do whatever it takes to heal your subconscious mind.

Inherited Emotional Stress and Epigenetics

While working temporarily for a genetic testing and coaching company, I was able to witness the true impact of stress on your cells and DNA. Many of the people whose charts I was working on, had gene mutations and other problems with the genetics they inherited. Some of them had either methylation problems or other health problems and some of them had no signs of health problems yet, but they were warned that they had to take the steps necessary to prevent any future health problems. Inherited emotional stress is emotional stress that happened to your parents and ancestors before you were born and went into their germ cells (eggs and sperm) and was passed down to you. Some of this inherited stress can take the form of inherited mental issues like anxiety and depression and others can take the form of breast cancer. Conventional medicine holds the viewpoint that we are all controlled by our genes and that the genetics we inherited from our parents and ancestors determines the fate of our health.

According to the studies on epigenetics done by world renowned cellular biologists, including Dr. Bruce Lipton, this is not the truth. Our fate is not sealed by what we have inherited through our genetics; instead, our fate is in our own hands. For those of you who haven't heard about epigenetics before, it is the study of inherited changes in phenotype (appearance) or gene expression caused by mechanisms other than changes in the underlying DNA sequence. In a blog called Epigenetics that appeared on his website in 2012, Dr. Lipton stated:

"The AMA protocol is to regard our physical body like a machine, in the same way that an auto mechanic regards a car. When the parts break, you replace them—a transplant, synthetic joints, and so on—and those are medical miracles. The problem is that while they have an understanding that the mechanism isn't working, they're blaming the vehicle for what went wrong. They believe that the vehicle, in this case our bodies, is controlled by genes. But guess what? They don't take into consideration that there's actually a driver in that car. The new science, epigenetics, reveals that the vehicles—or the genes—aren't responsible for the breakdown. It's the driver."

What Dr. Lipton is talking about is that even if you inherit stress and also a propensity for certain illness through your genes, you are in control of the eventual outcome. In the example of inherited control genes, the genes have an on/off switch that is flipped on by you and your emotional stress, beliefs or negative thoughts. The control genes control the expression of other genes. Basically you are in control of whether you ever get the inherited cancer or not. It is up to you to watch and modify your thoughts as well as prevent, delete and manage all of the emotional stress in your life.

Many years ago before I had ever heard of Dr. Lipton, my mother-in-law, who was a hospital nurse for many decades, said "We are all dealt a new hand of cards when we are born. Just because your parents had something, it doesn't mean you will ever get it." I have to agree 100% with my mother-in-law. Every allopathic medical professional may not agree with Dr. Lipton's conclusions, but his research and the study of epigenetics is making a big enough impact on the medical industry that changes are happening in medical school curriculum.

There have been several research studies done on how stress impacts DNA. A group led by Drs. James Potash and Gary Wand at the Johns Hopkins University School of Medicine conducted a scientific study to see how stress hormones affect genes central to the HPA axis through genetic modifications, which are changes to DNA that don't alter sequences but influence gene expression. The researchers in this study found that chronic exposure to a stress hormone causes modifications to DNA in the brains of mice, prompting changes in gene expression. The findings showed how chronic stress affects human behavior. The researchers also tested methylation levels of genes after they were exposed to stress hormones. This is a common epigenetic modification that affects gene expression.

In the September 2010 issue of Endocrinology, the researchers reported that mice given corticosterone (stress hormones) appeared more anxious during a maze test. Chronic exposure to the stress hormone altered the expression of their genes and created higher levels of a genetic variation that is seen with posttraumatic stress disorder and mood disorders. Dr. Potash said, "This gets at the mechanism through which we think epigenetics is important. Epigenetic marks added to DNA through life experience may prepare an animal for future events. If you think of the stress system as preparing you for fight or flight, you might imagine that these epigenetic changes might prepare you to fight harder or flee faster the next time you encounter something stressful."

The results of this study and many more studies on epigenetics show us how cellular memories of a traumatic event can travel through generations. It's important for us to understand how our emotional stress impacts our brain and leads to mood disorders, anxiety and other problems. We all have various levels of stress that go into our cellular memory and DNA, to be passed down to our children. Basically, we are giving our children and many generations of children, mental health issues, genetic mutations and methylation problems because of our own emotional stress.

All of the research suggests that epigenetic changes play a role in this process. To explain this in easier terms, every cell in the human body has a "brain" or memory. Every negative thought, emotion, trauma, belief and episode of stress is stored forever in your cellular memory unless you do work to clear it out. Cellular stress caused by traumatic experiences and your negative thoughts, beliefs and emotions will stay in your body until you clear it out and heal it. If you never do anything about it and then you have a child, that child risks inheriting your cellular stress.

Why explain this? Because it's important for you to know that your current mental and physical health issues could possibly be inherited through genetics from your parents and ancestors. It's also important for you to know how epigenetics works so that if you are young enough to have babies, you take steps to clear and heal your own genetic issues and also help your children to do the same. Even if you are older, you can help your children and grandchildren. I also want you to remember that you know that you have a new deck of cards and you can play your hand however you want. You can prevent getting any of the things you may have inherited through epigenetics and prevent passing these health issues down to future generations, by learning how to change your thoughts and beliefs, reprogram your brain for positive thinking and use the information in this book to manage stress.

You can prevent most problems in life by arming yourself with knowledge and taking action. I have recently had my genetic testing done to find out what gene mutations and genetic problems I have inherited from my ancestors. It was interesting to see what was in there, but I also know that I am in 100% control of the outcomes of my genetics. I recommend that everyone find this information out if they are able. The company I used for genetic testing is http://23andme.com. They can tell you what your DNA says about you and your family. Then you take the results to your M.D. or a genetics counselor who can help you review the information, explain it and create a plan to keep healthy.

You may be able to heal and clear your cellular memories and cellular stress that you have created by using one or more of the many new energy healing modalities that are available today. There are more and more new techniques coming out every day to help people heal their cellular stress and possibly prevent health problems from being passed down through your epigenetics. Here is a list of the modalities that I am currently aware of for healing your cellular and cellular stress:

Meditation

Psych-K

Body-Talk

Healing Codes

Emotion Codes

Theta Clearing

EFT (Emotional Freedom Techniques)

Pranic Healing

Quantum Touch

Reiki

Neuro Stress Release

Cellular Memory Release

Hypnotherapy
Prayer and connecting with God
Integrative Energy Therapy

Please keep in mind that this list is only the modalities and techniques that I am aware of for healing your cellular memory and preventing; there may be other excellent options that are not on this list.

Emotional Stress Caused by Past Lives

Since I tend to be very analytical and a lover of science, I have always been a little skeptical about things and usually need to have proof before I believe in something. I never used to believe in past lives. Then I started having very detailed dreams of being back in different time periods in history. The dreams always took place in different places around the world. I would have the same dreams over and over again. I thought these were only dreams, but the details in the dreams were mind blowing. I could see houses in full detail with cabinetry, furnishings and pictures on the walls. I could see gardens or land around the house and the countryside around the house. I got an idea of what part of my country I may have been in or what part of the world I may have been in. I started questioning my dreams and wondering if they were something more than just dreams.

For many years I dreamed that I was running down a dark alley in New York City. I have never been to New York City before, but strangely I could see everything of New York in full detail. I saw a gang of men chasing me and then I fell forward and it went black for a few seconds and then transitioned to my body flying over New York City like a bird looking down on everything. What I didn't know then, was that I was seeing my death in my very last life. After giving birth to my children, my intuitive, clairaudient and other metaphysical gifts really kicked in and I was able to tap into my higher self, spirit guides and angels and finally have answers to all of my questions. I learned that the dreams I was having were not dreams. I also learned that when I dreamed at night I could tell the difference between a past life memory and a regular dream, because I am able to find a mirror and see what I looked like. I certainly did not look like my current self. In each of these visions I had different skin color, different hair and features, different body type and sometimes different nationality. When I had a normal dream, I was me and when I was having a past life memory, I was someone completely different.

Then, I began to channel information from my guides and angels regarding the details of each of my past lives. I was able to look up the information I received in history books and on the internet to prove that the information was accurate. I knew I was not crazy or having a wild imagination, but I had a few family members and friends who thought I was, so I had to prove it to myself without a doubt that I was having past life memories. I did this, by hiring a hypnotherapist who specialized in past life regression. Sure enough I was able to go back into past lives under hypnosis and see them in full detail. Over the years, I have used several hypnotherapists and one of them was intuitive. It was such a thrill for me to not only prove to myself that I was actually having past life memories, but my newest hypnotherapist was so intuitive that she was able to see my visions at the same time and confirm what I was seeing.

What does all this have to do with Past Life Emotional Stress? Well, here is how I found out about past life emotional stress. After my mom and dad passed away, I developed many health problems from the stress, including massive allergies. There is a wonderful healing modality called Body Talk whose practitioner uses a combination of Eastern and Western holistic medicine and energy medicine. They speak with your body and cells to find out what past life stress, subconscious stress, or epigenetically-inherited stress is causing your current health problem. Once they bring it up to the surface, they reprogram your body and cells to heal and clear it out.

About 3 or 4 years ago, I started seeing a Body Talk practitioner who helped me clear and heal many of my health problems, including most of my allergies. During Body Talk sessions, past life stress can come up for clearing. I had many past life emotional stress issues come up and once they were healed, my health problems mysteriously disappeared. Doctors were amazed that these problems would just go away without any medication or treatments, but I knew that something supernatural had happened.

I used to have a deep fear of swimming in a pool, lake or the ocean in water deeper than where I could touch the bottom. I always had to have my feet able to touch bottom with my head out of the water in order to feel comfortable. My fear was so bad that every time I tried to go snorkeling in the ocean with my family, I would have an anxiety attack. During one of my Body Talk sessions, we discovered that I had drowned in several of my past lives. Those past life drownings were causing my fear. We did some energy healing on the past life memories. A short time after the healing session, I went on a vacation to the island of Kauai and went snorkeling with my family. For the first time in my life, my fear was gone and I was able to snorkel without any anxiety. I felt calm and relaxed. I knew it was because I healed my past life stress around drowning.

There was one major health issue that was a result of my parents' death that was interfering with my life daily. I went from doctor to doctor and none of them could give me any help for this health problem. I went to my Body Talk practitioner hoping she could help me, but no matter how many Body Talk sessions I had, that health problem would not go away. I was telling my hypnotherapist friend about my problem and she recommended we try a past life regression to see if we could clear it. Of course I agreed. When under hypnosis, I was able to uncover a lifetime in Cornwall England, where I was pregnant. Since my hypnotherapist was intuitive she was seeing what I was seeing at the same time. In fact, we both said, "pregnant" at the same time. I don't want to go into details about this experience in this book, but the important thing is that we were able to find the exact cause of my current health problem and a large phobia I had related to the health problem. Once I was able to bring this up and release it for healing, my phobia went away and my major health problem started to go away. Each week and month, it got better and better. Today, it's gone. It's funny how I spent 9 years trying to heal this with doctors, health practitioners and my own energy healing methods and did not get any results. Then after releasing that one past life experience, I was able to finally heal. If that is not proof of past life emotional stress, I don't know what is.

So what exactly is Past Life Emotional Stress (PLES)? PLES is basically any traumatic situation or emotionally stressful thing that happens to you in a past lifetime. This experience can be carried with you into your next lifetime and your next, until it is healed or cleared.

Since my parents died, I have also had a few near death experiences (NDE's), where I was dead for a few minutes and went to the other side and back. As a result of those experiences, I have learned many things, including the reason why we have such thing as reincarnation. I learned that God is the vibration of unconditional love. God is the great I Am, existing everywhere. God is in the past, present and future all at the same time. God unconditionally loves me, everyone and everything he/she has ever created. The most important thing I learned, is that we are all divine eternal beings having a human experience and our soul (life force or energy body) never dies but it goes go on forever. This soul has the ability to come back in many incarnations or lives if it wants to. The reason why we come to earth and into our human bodies is to have learning experiences and grow closer to our creator (God). The planet Earth is a giant classroom and we are here to learn. Not everyone gets reincarnated, because reincarnation is a choice that your soul makes.

We are co-creating our lives with God, who loves us unconditionally. That Creator allows us to have these multiple life experiences so that our souls can raise our vibration and gain eternal wisdom. Each of our souls is a unique thumbprint of God and we each have our own personal journey that we are on. We are all connected to one another through the great universal consciousness and energy of creation, which is why you hear the term Karma quite often. Because we are all connected, anything we do or say impacts ourselves and everyone else who is connected to this great universal consciousness of creation.

We are also equal to one another. No human being, no matter what race or color, no matter what religion, job, education or breeding is better than another. We are just souls, striving to be more advanced souls and we are all at different places in our learning. Some of us learn slower and some of us are quick studies. We all share a common goal of wanting happiness, unconditional love and becoming closer to our Creator. Each time we live another life on Earth or in other places, we are learning the lessons that get us closer to our goal of becoming more and more like Christ Consciousness and our Creator God. Some religions teach a message of duality that God is separate from us and sits on some high pedestal judging us. This is not true, since God is the vibration and frequency of unconditional love and God is all around us and also part of us. There is no separation, there is only oneness. Once people embrace that idea, their life is transformed. When you believe in the duality, you become separated from Source and you miss out on that unconditional love and support that your Creator longs to give you.

You may not believe in or know about past lives and may practice a religion where you were told it's wrong to believe this information. That is perfectly fine and I respect your opinion and beliefs. I am not here to convince you and you have to make up your own mind.

However, there are amazing amounts of evidence and proof that reincarnation exists. There are many millions of documented psychological cases and studies, where people have had memories of past lives or seen past lives under hypnotherapy. The concept of past life regression has been around since the time of the ancient Greeks. Sigmund Freud is the father of modern day Past Life Regression in the early 1900's. He came up with the idea that by making the unconscious conscious, one could restore choice and bring about healing. He discovered the link between past trauma and present symptoms and called it Psychic Determinism. He established that our past experiences determine our present behavior. Sigmund Freud's work changed psychotherapy forever and is the basis of regression work.

Austrian psychoanalyst Otto Rank, who was a friend and close colleague of Freud's, came up with a focus on birth memories. Later, Carl Jung came up with the concept of a Collective Unconscious and Archetypes (universal patterns). In the 1920's and 1930's, Edgar Cayce brought reincarnation to the public stage through his channeling of past lives. Since I too am now able to channel past life information, I have read most of Edgar Cayce's work and have much respect and admiration for what he did. Over 20 years ago, I did not have this ability of channeling information and was much more skeptical about the idea of past lives. In 1927, Paul Brunton wrote about a technique that the yogis developed in India, to tune into past-lives. Austrian psychoanalyst Wilhelm Reich made a contribution to the reincarnation movement, by his classification of Character Structures. The psychoanalytical practice of Past Life Regression really took off like crazy in the 1960's and 1970's and since then it has become a standard part of the mental health toolkit.

Reincarnation is a subject that has been taught in several of the world's religions for thousands of years. In Buddhism, one's current reincarnation is referred to as Samsara, the latest turn of The Wheel of Existence, the Perpetual Wandering. I know many wellrespected and intelligent people who have complete intact memories of their past lives. Many of these people have healed health problems and emotional issues as a result of doing past life regression hypnosis. They found out what stressful event happened to them in their past life, came to terms with it and cleared it out. Once they did that, their body or emotions were healed. Even if you don't believe in past lives, you cannot discount real healing experiences that many people have had and that have been validated by mental health practitioners, doctors and other witnesses. I personally have had several healings take place over the years as a result of clearing past life info.

But what does all of this reincarnation information mean for you? Simple. If you have any fears, phobias, addictions, mental or physical health problems that cannot be healed no matter how many doctors or modalities you try, chances are that it involves an issue from a past life. If you want to find out for sure and take some action, here's a list of resources, modalities and methods you can try out to find out the past life source of a current emotional or physical illness in your body. There may be other modalities out there, but his list contains the things I have tried out or researched extensively.

You will want to research these all for yourself on the internet:

Learn how to practice meditation, quiet your mind, develop your intuitive gifts and get in touch with God, Ascended Masters, your higher self, guides and angels to get the answers you need. This is how I started out.

Find a Mental Health Counselor or Hypnotherapist who specializes in past life regression therapy and go try it out. If you are afraid of hypnotherapy, please do not worry, because you are 100% in control of your mind and body the entire time. Your mind has protection built in that will not allow you to do anything you would not want to do. Some people have a belief that the devil or a demon will take them over when they are under hypnosis and some people think that their practitioner can do something to them. All of these ideas are wrong beliefs and false information because you are in 100% control the entire time.

Body Talk practitioner. To find out what "Body Talk" is and where to find a practitioner in your area, please visit, https://www.bodytalksystem.com/learn/bodytalk/
Psych-K, created by Robert Williams, who wrote Psych-K, The Missing Peace in Your Life (https://www.psych-k.com/). This is practiced by Dr. Bruce Lipton and he even teaches with Rob Williams.

EMDR (Eye Movement Desensitization and Reprocessing), is a psychotherapy treatment that was originally designed to alleviate the distress associated with traumatic memories.

EFT (Emotional Freedom Technique). This is a practice that involves tapping on certain energy meridians while saying a sentence or mantra to yourself. There are many free videos on the web on how to do this. There are also millions of EFT practitioners.

Sometimes Reiki, Chakra Balancing, Pranic Healing, Qi Gong and other energy healing can remove past life trauma/emotional stress.

Emotion Codes, Anahata Codes or The Healing Codes. These are all different from one another but use a code theory for healing emotional stress. There are books on the Emotion Codes and Healing Codes, so you can learn to do them yourself or hire a practitioner to teach you how.

See a psychic, intuitive or channel who specializes in past lives, a modern day Edgar Cayce. Luckily, we live in an age where there are millions of people on the earth with these gifts, so it's easy to find someone to help you. Please beware of phony psychics and scammers. Unfortunately, for every good metaphysical practitioner, there are several bad ones. Make sure to pick someone with a long history and track record of success, someone who comes highly recommended and has testimonials to prove their success.

Spirituality – The Soul's Way of Healing Emotional Stress

In the last section I mentioned a few things about my own spiritual experiences and spiritual development that were driven by my health problems and my near-death experiences (NDE's). Spirituality is one of the most important tools for managing emotional stress. Without any kind of spirituality in your life, you are kind of like an empty vessel that needs to be filled up inside. Spirituality is what keeps many people who have sadness and tragedy in their lives from committing suicide. Back when I was younger and had a very difficult life, I was unhappy and depressed. I think the only thing that kept me moving forward and prevented me from deep depression or suicide was my Spirituality.

I think of Spirituality as the food that feeds our soul and makes it dance. Spirituality and Religion are two completely different things. You can have one and not have the other, but the two also go together and overlap. Some people are religious but not spiritual and some people don't practice a religion but they are spiritual. Many people don't know or understand what spirituality is exactly. Even some people who practice spirituality don't fully know the definition. That is because it is such a broad idea and field, that it's almost impossible to create an exact definition. To shed some light on the subject, here are some definitions of spirituality from Georgetown University's National Center for Cultural Competence:

"The experience or expression of the sacred" (Adapted from Random House Dictionary of the English Language, 1967).
"The search for transcendent meaning" – can be expressed in religious practice or expressed exclusively in their relationship to nature, music, the arts, a set of philosophical beliefs, or relationships with friends and family" (Astrow et al. 2001).

"Individual search for meaning" Bowen and Williams 1993).
"The search for meaning in life events and a yearning for connectedness to the universe" (Coles 1990).

"A person's experience of, or a belief in, a power apart from his or her own existence" (Mohr 2006).
"A quality that goes beyond religious affiliation that strives for inspiration, reverence, awe, meaning and purpose, even in those who do not believe in God. The spiritual dimension tries to be in harmony with the universe, strives for answers about the infinite, and comes essentially into focus in times of emotional stress, physical (and mental) illness, loss, bereavement and death" (Murray and Zentner 1989:259).

"Refers to a broad set of principles that transcend all religions. Spirituality is about the relationship between ourselves and something larger. That something can be the good of the community or the people who are served by your agency or school or with energies greater than ourselves. Spirituality means being in the right relationship with all that is. It is a stance of harmlessness toward all living beings and an understanding of their mutual interdependence." (Kaiser 2000)

I like the description of Spirituality that Larry Culliford posted in Psychology Today in 2011. He said, "Spirituality is not a thing, object or specimen that can be dissected and analyzed. You can look at it as something free of institutional structures and hierarchies, not so much about dogma and beliefs as about attitudes, values and practices, about what motivates you (us) at the deepest level, influencing how you think and behave, helping you find a true and useful place in your community, culture and in the world. Spirituality can be thought of as the 'active ingredient' of major world religions (and some humanistic ideologies too)." Larry asks us to look at spirituality as an adventure playground, a place to learn in and have fun and a place in which to extend yourself and grow. He also said, "Spirituality cannot be explored using scientific methods because it involves deeply personal, subjective experiences, and in this it differs from the over-riding ambition of science: to be objective. Both are necessary and appropriate, complementary formulas for discovering ourselves, each other, our environment, the universe... and especially an enduring sense of purpose and meaning."

Every person has their own unique way of practicing spirituality. There is no right or wrong way to do it; the important element is that you have spiritual practices or rituals you do every day, as it will help you to heal your body, mind and spirit, grow closer to God, experience your connectivity to everyone and everything, and prevent and heal emotional stress. You need to determine what your spiritual practices or learning will be. No one else can make that decision for you. I have several things I do daily to be a spiritual person and practice spirituality.

These things I do have helped me to prevent and heal my own stress, heal my body and grow much closer to God, my angels and guides and higher self. Here is my personal list:

Practice, use and implement my Spiritual Laws (See below)
Pray every day
Meditate often

Listen to and follow my inner guidance and higher self.
Listen to and follow God, Christ, my angels and guides.
Use Crystals for healing, accessing higher vibrational energies, facilitating meditation

Attend church or sometimes go to a Buddhist temple, for the purpose of community, meditation and praying with others. Scientific studies have shown that group prayer creates an enormous energy field that can be seen with special devices and photography, reaching all the way up to the sky.

Now, I would like to share with you my Spiritual Laws and Principles for managing stress and living a happier life. This is partially a recap of some of the topics I discussed earlier in the section on conscious emotional stress. I have learned some of these laws from other teachers and some of the greatest masters who have walked the earth, so you may recognize or know some of these already. Some of them are taken right from the Bible. I don't expect you to follow and use my laws. I can only attest to the fact that these laws have greatly transformed my life and the life of my coaching clients who I have taught them too.

Kimberly's Spiritual Laws and Principles:

Spend time each day in prayer, reflection or meditation to connect to my Creator and hear his/her voice. "Be still and know, 'I Am'."

Love myself unconditionally the way that God loves me.
Be unconditional love to every person I meet.

I am co-creating my life along with God, by every thought I think, every word I say out of my mouth and every action I take. I choose to only create good in my life. I am the conscious presence controlling my thoughts, speech and life. No one else has control over me except for myself and Creator God.

Take care of my body because it is the temple of the Holy Spirit.

I only use the words "I Am" with positive words and statements because "I Am" is God's name and every time I use those two words together, I am manifesting and creating my reality. I Am is the creating force of God and I am creating every time I say, I Am.

I always speak my truth, stand in the truth and follow The Truth. I align myself with others who also do the same. I never lie and do not spend time with people who lie because it lowers and drains my energy.

Be kind and compassionate to every person and animal, no matter what the situation is. Even be kind and compassionate to people who are mean, rude or disrespectful to me because I do not know where they are on their spiritual journey, which may be influencing their bad behavior.

Show people grace and mercy because God gives me his/her grace and mercy every day.

Always forgive and release everyone who has hurt me in the past, present and future.

Always remember negative events from the past, like the Holocaust, but never focus on them. Instead learn lessons from the experience, forgive the people involved, release the negative emotions and move forward. Make sure that these negative events do not happen to myself, my family or anyone else ever again.

I will never fear, because fear is false evidence appearing real. Fear is an illusion that will harm my body, mind and spirit. I know that I am always safe and protected by my God, my Guardian Angels and the Universe.

I am a limitless being and I can do anything I put my intention on that is for my highest good. I do not accept the limits that other people place on me or limiting thoughts and beliefs that have been put into my mind by others since I was conceived.

I am grateful for my life and everything in it. I practice gratitude daily by praying and thanking my Creator. I show my gratitude to every person who assists me in any way. I keep a gratitude journal to always remember what I am grateful for so that when times are difficult or things don't go my way, I can refer to my gratitude list for encouragement.

I know my purpose on earth and every day I only chose to do things that are in alignment with my purpose.

I serve and help people and animals every day through either charity or actions, because through service I am building my treasure chest in heaven.

I do everything I can to make sure I leave this earth a better place than it was before I came into it.

There is really no such thing as failure. There is only a series of learning experiences on the road to success. When things don't work out the way I expect them to, I learn from the experiences, make changes or adjustments and keep moving forward towards my goals. I cannot have success without having some failures.

Every time I judge or criticize someone I pull far away from God. Every human is a reflection of some aspect of me. No human is perfect or the same as I am. I am no better than the person I am judging or criticizing. I need to work on myself and not worry about other people's journey.

I cannot change people. I need to be the change I want to see.

Time flies by fast and so does my life in this body. Every day that I am alive is a gift, so I need to enjoy the little joys of life.
It is important for me to tell my loved ones I love them regularly because I never know when they will be gone. I never want to have any regrets.

It's important to always have my spiritual priorities in order so I put God first, myself second, my family third and my career fourth.

It is important for me to take care of myself first before taking care of everyone else, because if I get sick and die, I won't be here to take care of family, friends and clients.

I look for the good in everything always. I always try to find the silver lining in the cloud.

Whenever anything negative happens to me, I always ask, "What can I learn from this and how can I use this experience to improve myself and to help others?" Make lemonade out of the lemons!

I can never expect any person to make me happy. It is not up to others to make me happy. I am in control of my happiness. I create my own happiness and my happiness is a choice and a state of mind. I know that

THE REAL FOUNTAIN OF YOUTH |199

no material possession will give me long term happiness. My happiness will always come from things like bird watching or having a picnic with my husband, meditation and connecting with my Higher Self, learning new things, having positive experiences and doing service for mankind.

The spiritual laws and principles you have just read, are my personal list that I live by every day. If you are already practicing something similar, then that's great! If you are not practicing any type of spirituality, you may want to consider doing some research into spirituality and try out a few things, or feel free to use my list. Experiment and see how things work for you. Never force yourself to do something unless it's for your highest good. Whenever you force yourself to do things you don't want to do, there will be resistance and more stress in your life.

The purpose of these spiritual practices is to help you reduce stress. If you try something out and it doesn't feel comfortable, doesn't work for you or you don't like it, please stop doing it and try something else. Be open to exploring new things and new ideas. Have fun and look at your life and spirituality as a great adventure.

Important Books for Healing Emotional Stress

There is an emotional cause to almost every mental or physical health problem. As a medical intuitive, health and life coach and energy healer, I have had hundreds of people come to me over the years, because they are unable to get help from their doctors for their health problems. Once I work with them, we find an emotional root cause or sometimes several or more emotional root causes and we work on healing the emotional stress. Once we heal the emotional root cause, the clients are able to heal their body, mind and spirit. God created our bodies with the ability to heal, but stress blocks your healing ability. When you start managing all of the stress in your life, you will notice that you are suddenly able to heal things that have seemed impossible to heal before.

You will also notice your immune system strengthening and that you do not get sick as much. Some people never get sick when they have healthy, happy emotions and are able to manage, prevent, delete and reduce all of their stress. Back in the days when I was very anxious and stressed out, before I went on my own personal healing journey, I was frequently sick with everything from colds, flus and sinus infections to mystery illnesses that doctors could not diagnose. Once I learned and practiced all of the things in this book on myself, my health improved and mystery illnesses disappeared. I rarely ever get colds or flus and haven't had a sinus infection in many years. I am so happy and grateful to have a healthy body.

The most important thing that has helped me on my healing journey over the years, has been the emotional healing books that I have read. There are hundreds of books on the market that can help you with emotional healing. It's up to you to research and find out which books resonate with you. However, I am now going to share with you my personal list of books that has helped me over the years. These books will remain on my book shelves forever. I recommend these books to all of my coaching clients and for a few years I even loaned them out to clients. Unfortunately, the clients loved my books so much, they would not return them. I had to replace my books regularly, which got very expensive. I finally stopped lending out my books and now give my clients this same list I am giving you.

Kimberly's Favorite Books for Managing Emotional Stress:

You Can Heal Your Life – by: Louise Hay
Heal Your Body A to Z – by: Louise Hay
The Biology of Belief – by: Bruce H. Lipton, PhD
Change Your Thoughts Change Your Life – by: Dr. Wayne W. Dyer

THE REAL FOUNTAIN OF YOUTH |201

I Am Wishes Fulfilled – by: Dr. Wayne W. Dyer
Every book that has been written by Deepak Chopra, M.D. – too many too list
The Healing Codes – by: Dr. Alexander Loyd, PhD, ND and Ben Johnson, MD, Do, NMD 8. The Emotion Code – by: Dr. Bradley Nelson

Your Body Speaks Your Mind – by: Deb Shapiro
What's Your Body Telling You – by: Steve Sisgold
Instant Emotional Healing – Acupressure for the Emotions – by: George J. Pratt, PhD and Peter T. Lambrou, PhD
The Intention Experiment – by: Lynn McTaggart

Affirmations – by: Stuart Wilde (all of Stuart Wilde's books are good reads)
The Power of Positive Thinking – by: Norman Vincent Peale
The Big Leap – by: Gay Hendricks
Ask And It Is Given – by: Esther and Jerry Hicks, the Teachings of Abraham

The I Am Discourses – by: Saint Germain
Mind Power Into the 20th Century - by: John Kehoe
U78The Power of Awareness – by: Neville Goddard
E – Squared – by: Pam Grout

The Miracle of Mindfulness – by: Thich Nhat Hanh
Mindfulness in Plain English – by: Bhante Henepola Gunaratana
Healing Anxiety and Depression – by: Daniel G. Amen, M.D. and Lisa C. Routh, M.D.
Worried No More – Help and Hope for Anxious Children – by: Aureen Pinto Wagner, PhD

Battlefield of the Mind – by: Joyce Meyer

Freedom From Worry and Anxiety – by: Joyce Meyer (Joyce has many other books about worry, fear, anxiety and depression and they are all good)

A Few Last Words on Managing Emotional Stress

This chapter discussed many personal, intense and some taboo subjects regarding your emotions and thinking. It's important for you to take your time to absorb all of this information that you just learned. Do not rush into applying what you have learned into your life until you have fully processed the information and feel comfortable enough to move forward.

You may be ready, right now, to start implementing this info or you may take a while longer to move forward. We all have unique ways of learning. Make sure to go easy on yourself, without any judgment. When you begin to implement things from this chapter you may start to notice and experience some shifts and changes in your life, health and relationships. Some people may experience slight or mild changes and others may experience huge transformational changes. Your friends and family may notice that your personality or something else about you has changed and they may make a comment. When someone notices your changes, give yourself a big hug for creating the changes in a way that people noticed.

If you get stuck or it is difficult for you to implement any of the ideas in this chapter, you may want to consider working with a coach, mental health practitioner or other professional who can help you to implement the information in this chapter.

You may have noticed that I did not have a section on depression, which is a rampant problem in our society today. There are a few reasons why

I did not cover this subject. First of all, there is already a rich literature on depression. I recommend any of the books by Daniel G. Amen, M.D., who is has been on PBS and is a world renowned doctor of psychiatry. In fact I recommend you read all of his books on mental health and the brain, because they are all terrific. The other reason why I did not talk about depression is because it's basically a mental illness caused by stress. If you follow what you have learned in this book, it may be possible for you to prevent or heal depression.

One final word on emotional stress: A Course in Miracles by The Foundation for Inner Peace, states that there are only two major emotions that all of the other emotions stem from and those two emotions are love and fear. The positive emotions and thoughts come from love and the negative ones come from fear. The best way for you to manage stress and live a happier and healthier life, is for you to strive for love in all areas of your life and relationships, as well as in your thoughts and actions. If you focus on everything being lovebased, you can have peace in your life.

Activities for Managing Emotional Stress

Pushing the Delete Button on stress. Take a piece of paper and write the word, "Delete" at the top of the page. Make a list of all the things, events, activities, chores, jobs, people and places that cause you emotional stress and that you can get out of your life or maybe delegate to someone else. A few examples: If watching the news before bedtime gets you emotionally upset, then turn off the T.V. and don't watch it; if having a conversation on the phone with your mother in law is upsetting, don't talk with that person anymore; if going bowling with your husband is embarrassing and stressful, then stop going; if having lunch with co-workers is annoying, then have lunch by yourself; if you don't like shopping in the mall, order your things on the internet.

I am sure you can think of plenty of items to put on your delete list If this exercise is difficult for you, then you have to love yourself enough to want to take care of yourself, stand up for yourself, create boundaries and have the strength and courage to say "no more". Once you have your list completed, try to pick one or more items each day to delete from your life. Some of the things you may be able to delegate or hand over to someone else to do. When you have deleted all of the things on your list, start paying attention to how much lighter and more peaceful you feel. Pay attention to how your life and possibly health changes. Some of the things on your list may be making you sick, so you will feel better when you get rid of them.

Rewire your brain for positive thinking. Spend a few days or preferably a week keeping track of every time you think or say something negative. Keep a notepad and pen in your pocket at all times. Anytime you think a negative thought or say anything negative, write it down on your note pad. At the end of the day, take all of the things you have said or thought about and write a positive affirmation. For example, if you said to yourself, "I hate my thighs," you will write down a positive affirmation to counteract it like, "I love myself just the way I am." Try to notice a pattern and see if there are similar negative thoughts and statements you are thinking and saying over and over again.

Next step: once you have the positive affirmations, remember them and the next time you think the same negative thought, immediately counteract it with your positive affirmation. This will protect your body from the stress caused by negative thinking and speaking. You can say your affirmations to yourself or out loud. They are more powerful when you say them out loud, but you probably won't want to do that when someone is listening.

Pick one new modality for emotional healing and start using it daily. You will have to do some internet research to learn about each of the modalities and find one that resonates with you. If it doesn't make you feel better emotionally within a few days, then try something else.

Some of the many emotional healing modalities include: Emotional Freedom

Techniques, Meditation, Mindfulness, Healing Codes, Anahata Codes, Psych-K, Cognitive Behavioral Therapy, EMDR, Body Talk and more. Just web-search the words Emotional Healing, Emotional Healing Modalities or similar.

Once you find something that works well, try a few more things so that you have a bunch of modalities to choose from to help you. Ways to tell you are getting better include: feeling less angry, feeling happier, calmer, more peaceful, quieter brain, less overwhelm, less anxiety, no panic attacks. The modalities I personally have had the most success with are Psych-K, Emotion Codes, Body Talk, Cognitive Behavioral Therapy, Mindfulness and Meditation. I have used all of those very successfully on myself.

Emotional healing and manifestation mantra. Mantras are a great way to reprogram your brain for happiness and success. You can also use mantras to manifest what you want in your life. I have spent years trying to come up with different mantras that work well for me and my clients. I finally found one mantra that covers many areas at once and will help you to create what you want in your life. If you like my mantra and it resonates with you. Please write this mantra down on several 3" X 5" cards and put them up in different places at home and work where you can see them daily. Say this mantra as many times a day as possible to re-write your negative thinking and so you can start manifesting what you want in your life.

You may also take my mantra and rewrite it in a way that works best for you. There are no limits to how you can use this for your highest good.

"I am attracting and receiving love, success, perfect health and abundance in every area of my life"

CHAPTER 4
CHEMICAL STRESS

Toxins that are in our foods, beverages, drugs, air, clothing, cosmetics, air and water are making us sick, causing health problems like cancers and other killers. Since toxic chemicals harm our body and brain, they constitute a form of stress and are the 3rd major category of stress in the P.E.A.C.E. Stress Management System®.

We live in a time in history when our planet and our bodies are being polluted daily by toxic chemicals that did not exist before this last century. More and more toxic chemicals are invented in laboratories all over the world and put into our food supply, land and water every day. Toxic chemicals are a factor in the exponential increase in childhood disease. Cancer is the leading cause of death (after accidents) in children younger than 15 years old in the United States today. Childhood cancer rates have been rising slightly for the past few decades. Autism, ADD, ADHD and other brain disorders are also on the rise in children. According to a report by the CDC (Centers for Disease Control and Prevention) in 2014, one in 68 U.S. children has an autism spectrum disorder (ASD), a 30% increase from 1 in 88 two years prior to that. Many people are pointing a finger at the toxins in our food, beverages and environment. In the last 22 years, there's been a 300% increase in allergies, a 300% increase in asthma, and a 400% increase in ADHD. One possible explanation for this rise in illness is chemicals.

The sole purpose for all of these toxic chemicals is corporate greed. If the profit created by the use of these things was taken away, there would no longer exist a need for these poisons on our planet. The chemical industry remains the largest industry in the world, with more than $770 billion in annual sales and more than $39 billion in capital expenditures. This means toxic chemical laws are more about protecting the chemical industry than they are about protecting public health. Unfortunately, we do not have much control over this, unless all of the people of the world were to band together and fight it.

Governments and big corporations control the fate of our health and our planet by creating these poisons and putting them into the land, the creatures of the planet and us. In Beijing China, the air is so polluted that you cannot see very far and most people have to wear masks on their face. Many major cities in the world have very poor air quality.

Even if we are unable to stop the toxic chemicals from going into the food supply, air and overall environment, there are still many things that each of us can do to protect ourselves and our pets and families and also detox from the toxic chemicals and heal. We do have control over our own bodies, our family's exposure and our family's health. I do my best to reduce my footprint on the planet by recycling, only dumping my trash into trash cans, not into streams, lakes, forests and parks, and using environmentally-safe products for personal care and in my home and garden.

Where Are the Toxic Chemicals Hiding?

Before I go into a detailed discussion about what you can do to protect yourself and your family from toxic chemicals, I would like to share with you a list of what either contains toxic chemicals or creates toxic chemicals. You may already know about some of these, and some of them may be a surprise to you.

The air we breathe (Smog, smoke, chem-trails and other air pollution)
Our water (fluoride, chlorine, pesticides, other chemicals, parasites and bacteria)
Our garage (Almost everything we store and use in the garage)

Cars, trucks, busses, boats, trains, motorcycles, cruise ships, airplanes and all types of transport that runs on fuel

Our home interior and contents (everything from the paint on the walls, insulation and carpeting to your furnishings)

Household cleaning items (everything from laundry soap to glass cleaner)

Utensils, plates, cups, pots, pans, storage containers, aluminum foil, plastic bags, plastic wrap and Styrofoam

The oceans, lakes and streams

Foods and beverages (alcohol, hydrogenated fats, caffeine, preservatives, additives, food colors, pesticides and more)

Prescription drugs, vitamins and supplements

Tobacco products

Stimulants and non-prescription drugs

Skin care products and cosmetics (everything from shampoo and lipstick to underarm deodorant)

Dental office (anesthesia, fillings, crowns, bridges, glues and other things used in dental offices)

Hospitals and doctor's offices

Shopping malls, airports, hotels, amusement parks and other crowded, closed environments

Clothing and shoes

Jewelry and accessories

Exposure to molds, fungus and dust (they can be toxic to your body, especially if you have allergies)

Manufacturing plants and factories

Gardening and farming supplies, soil and compost, sprays and other products used to support produce.

Treated wood and building materials
Fireplaces, burning fires, BBQ's, smokers
Heating and air-conditioning (HVAC) systems

Old lead plumbing
Asbestos in homes and other places
Mining operations

Ground soil that has been polluted by chemicals
Radon in granite countertops
Oil rigs and oil tankers (Gulf of Mexico and Exxon Valdez incidents)

Thousands of chemicals bombard your body daily from the atmosphere, your furniture, water, food and other sources that you cannot do anything about. In fact, scientists are saying that we use over 80,000 chemicals in the United States and we do not know how many can become a part of our chemical body burden. We do know that several hundred of these chemicals have been measured in people's bodies around the world.

Scientists estimate that everyone alive today carries within their body at least 700 contaminants, most of which have not been well studied. This is true whether we live in a rural or isolated area, in the middle of a large city, or near an industrialized area. According to an article that appeared in the New York Times in 2013, many Americans assume that their shampoos, detergents and other consumer products have been thoroughly tested and proved to be safe, but that assumption is wrong. Pharmaceuticals and pesticides have to be tested before they are put on the market, but industrial chemicals do not. Producers of these chemicals are rarely required to provide the federal government the information necessary for assessing safety.

Regulators, doctors, environmentalists and the chemical industry agree that the Toxic Substances Control Act, which is our country's main chemical safety law, needs to be changed. It has not been updated since the 1970's! According to Dr. Richard Denison, senior scientist at the Environmental Defense Fund, "Under this law, the E.P.A. can't even require testing to determine whether a risk exists without first showing a risk is likely.....It's the worst kind of Catch-22." Because of this, the majority of chemicals being used today have never been independently-tested for safety.

Some of the things on my list are totally within your control and you can protect yourself and your family from them. You can stop using tobacco, illegal drugs, stimulants and heavy amounts of alcohol. However, there are many items on this list that you have no control over. In those cases, you will have to minimize the effects of the toxic chemicals by doing a regular detox program. At the end of this chapter, I will share my recommendations for doing a safe and healthy detox. For now, let's focus on the items on the list. I will also give you advice for protecting yourself and your family from these dangers, where and when possible.

Chemicals and Toxins in Food, Beverages and Water
Meat and Produce

Many people don't know that most of the livestock and poultry in the U.S. and in some other countries are given antibiotics and hormones to make them get bigger, faster, and be disease-resistant. The antibiotics and hormones are also in milk products and eggs. Misuse and over-use of antibiotics speeds up the evolution of bacterial strains that are resistant to all our known antibiotics! This leads to bacterial infections in humans that are resistant to treatment. The hormones given to beef, pork and poultry have been scientifically shown to cause hormonal problems in humans of both sexes. It has also been scientifically linked to cancer.

To make matters worse, the animals are fed GM/GMO (genetically modified) grains that are suspected of causing everything from miscarriages in women, to cancer and other problems in humans and animals. GMO's are also in our produce. Most of the corn produced in the United States these days is GM along with many other vegetables, fruits and produce. Other countries, including Russia and most of the rest of Europe, have completely banned GM's and will not accept meat from the United States because of GM's and other things we put in our animals. GMO food is a concern because animal studies have shown organ damage, gastrointestinal and immune system disorders, accelerated aging and infertility. Human studies have shown that GM food can act as carriers for toxic substances that remain in our bodies long-term, possibly causing problems. Toxic insecticide produced by GM corn was found in the blood of pregnant women and their fetuses in studies.

After GMs were introduced in 1996, the percentage of Americans with three or more chronic illnesses jumped from 7% to 13% in just 9 years; food allergies skyrocketed, and disorders such as autism, reproductive disorders, digestive problems, and others are on the rise. There is not enough research to confirm GMs are a contributing factor, but it's clear to many people that GMs are not good for the human body. Most GM crops are loaded with deadly Roundup herbicides and farmers are increasing the amount of herbicides they apply every year. This harms our environment and is linked to sterility, hormone disruption, birth defects, and cancer. Not only do GM crops harm humans but they also harm birds, insects, amphibians, marine ecosystems, and soil organisms, even in small doses. GMs reduce biodiversity, pollute water resources, and are unsustainable.

The pesticides that are sprayed on crops, GM or not, are dangerous and harmful to every living thing. My recommendation is that you decide for yourself if GMs are okay for your family. If you don't think so, then vote with your feet by buying Non-GMO foods. Make sure that you check all of the labels, and shop at organic markets and local farms that do not use GMOs. Buy organic meat, produce, milk products and eggs, whenever possible. When you eat out at restaurants, focus on restaurants that prepare organic foods.

Beverages

Our most important drink is water. However, most of our water supply contains harmful substances. The water you are drinking may have everything from fluoride and chlorine to pesticides, drugs, parasites, bacteria and more. In 2015, scientists reported large amounts of heart and blood pressure drugs and anti-depressants in the drinking water supply because of all the people flushing their drugs down the toilet. Every time someone flushes drugs down the toilet, it eventually becomes part of drinking water, because our current public water treatment methods aren't set up to scrub these drugs out of the water like they remove other contaminants. Even with a septic system, the drugs can sometimes make it into the ground water and work their way into streams and waterways.

The best way to protect yourself and your family is to buy a state of the art water filter. Make sure that when you pick a water filter it removes as much harmful substances as possible. A good quality filer will remove everything from heavy metals, fluoride and chlorine to viruses and bacteria like E Coli, resistant cysts, cryptosporidium and giardia. The only thing that should ever be in your drinking water is what God intended it to have and that's trace minerals and H2O. Check reputable testing organizations like Consumer Reports to find a highly-rated water filtration system. Keep in mind that if there is chlorine in your water and you are taking a shower in that, your lungs and skin are absorbing the chlorine. Chlorine is used to kill bacteria in drinking and public water, so you will find it in public hot tubs and swimming pools as well. Chlorine is poisonous to all living things. If you are able to put in a whole-house filter, you can protect yourself from the effects of chlorine in the water while bathing and showering.

The fluoride that is added into the water in the United States to prevent dental decay in children has been linked to other health problems in children and adults. Many scientific studies have been conducted on the dangerous effects of fluoride on the body and brain. According to an article by Dr. Joseph Mercola, more people drink fluoridated water in the US alone, than in the rest of the world combined. In Western Europe, 97 percent of the population drinks non-fluoridated water. Fluoride has been banned by countries all over the world because of its toxic effects on all living creatures. According to Dr. Mercola's article, fluoridated countries do not have less tooth decay than non-fluoridated countries. The World Health Organization (WHO) has stated that there is no discernible difference in tooth decay between developed countries that fluoridate their water and those that do not. The decline in tooth decay the US has experienced over the last 60 years, which is often attributed to fluoridated water, has likewise occurred in all developed countries, most of which do not fluoridate their water. The reason why all countries have a decline in tooth decay regardless of their use of fluoride is probably do due to dental education, improvements in the dental field and more people taking care of their health. It is now widely recognized that fluoride's only justifiable benefit comes from topical contact with teeth (as in toothpaste), which the US Centers for Disease Control and Prevention (CDC) has acknowledged.

Adding it to water and pills, which are swallowed, offers little, if any, benefit to your teeth. According to FAN (The Fluoride Action Network), the fluoride supplements sometimes prescribed to those who are not drinking fluoridated water have not been approved by the

US Food and Drug Administration (FDA) for the prevention of tooth decay. In fact, the fluoride supplements that the FDA has reviewed have been rejected. FAN stated, "So with fluoridation, we are adding to the water a prescription-strength dose of a drug that has never been approved by the FDA." Many people think that fluoride improves your dental health, however according to a 500-page scientific review, fluoride is an endocrine disruptor that can affect your bones, brain, thyroid gland, pineal gland and even your blood sugar levels. There have been over 34 human and 100 animal studies linking fluoride to brain damage, including lower IQ in children. Studies have shown that fluoride toxicity can lead to a wide variety of health problems, including increased lead absorption, disruption of collagen synthesis, hyperactivity and/or lethargy, muscle disorders, thyroid disease, arthritis,

dementia, bone fractures caused by bone demineralization, and bone cancer (osteosarcoma). It also inactivates 62 enzymes and inhibits more than 100, inhibits the formation of antibodies, causes genetic damage and cell death, causes increased tumor and cancer incidence, disrupts the immune system, and damages sperm and other reproductive cells, leading to increased infertility. If this information doesn't make you run out and buy a water filter today, I'll be very surprised!

If you or your family members drink sodas and other canned or bottled beverages, you may be drinking a chemical cocktail. There is a laundry list of chemicals that appear in most store beverages, everything from food colorings and preservatives to artificial colors. Sodium benzoate and potassium benzoate, for instance, are preservatives that are sometimes added to sodas to prevent mold growth, but benzene is a known carcinogen. If you drink soda pop, which contains benzoates and you take vitamin C or Ascorbic acid, it creates benzene gas (toxic and deadly) in your intestines. Another preservative found in beverages is called Butylated Hydroxyanisole and is potentially cancer-causing. Diet drinks contain twice as many chemicals as regular drinks and have artificial sweeteners like Aspartame (NutraSweet, Equal), saccharin (Sweet'N Low, SugarTwin), and sucralose (Splenda). Artificial sweeteners have been linked to everything from hyperactivity in children and cancer to Gulf War syndrome. My recommendation is to read the labels on everything and try to focus on beverages like fruit juice, water and ice tea that are free from chemicals. If you really love your diet Coke, have it as a treat once in a while. Make sure you do not drink or eat anything with sodium benzoate or potassium benzoate at the same time that you take a vitamin C supplement or eat any citrus fruits or other foods containing ascorbic acid or vitamin C. By itself, there's no evidence the preservatives sodium benzoate or potassium benzoate cause any problems in people. However, when you mix any type of benzoate with ascorbic acid (vitamin C), a chemical reaction occurs. It turns the mixture into benzene. And benzene is a proven carcinogen that can cause cancer or other health issues.

In an effort to make their drinks more nutritious, many soft drink manufacturers are adding vitamin C to their drinks. And you'll also find the same problem with naturally occurring vitamin C in many canned juice drinks.

Another tip, is that if you are going to drink soda pop, go for the regular kind with sugar, because it has less chemicals than the diet types of drinks. I have two teenagers that drink a Coke to cure their headaches. Since I don't buy soda pop, this is a problem and they wind up going to the store and getting it for themselves. They want to drink the diet Coke, but I ask them to get the regular Coke instead, so they minimize their chemical exposure. As a mom I have to pick my battles, but I do my best to keep my kids healthy. Since diet drinks have the most chemicals of any beverage, it's best to stick with water, coffee, tea and iced tea. I like to drink fruit infused water throughout the day or iced green tea with some lemon and stevia. If you need to sweeten your coffee or tea, I recommend using Stevia or some honey, which are both natural.

Make sure to regulate your use of caffeine. Caffeine is considered a chemical stimulant. Humans love to drink things like coffee, tea, coke, Monster and other beverages that are loaded with caffeine. Some people drink them because they like the taste and some people drink them to stay awake and have more energy. The energy that caffeine gives is temporary and causes a huge slump in energy level later in the day. Small amounts of these drinks are okay, but if you drink too much caffeine (or consume it in other foods), you can create health problems. Large amounts of caffeine can cause hyperactivity, headaches, anxiety, upset stomach, ulcers, heart palpitations, high blood pressure and more. Every year thousands of people in the United States go to the emergency room with heart problems from energy drinks and other caffeinated products. If you already have high blood pressure, a heart arrhythmia or other heart problems, caffeine will exacerbate your problems. If you have an anxiety disorder, caffeine will make it worse. You need to find more healthy ways to wake up and give yourself energy. If you have health problems, you should not have caffeine. The healthy should be moderate. For any questions about caffeine, check with your doctor.

Limit your alcohol consumption to healthy amounts. Alcoholic beverages cause deadly auto crashes every year. Drinking too much alcohol can cause liver failure. Alcohol has also been linked to several types of cancers and it can also burn a hole through the stomach. On one hand, there have been studies showing that one glass of red wine, which contains resveratrol, is very good for your heart. On the other hand, some studies show that women who drink any amount of alcohol have a higher risk of breast cancer. When it comes to drinking alcohol, you have to use proper judgement. I personally like to have a glass of red wine with my dinner once in a while. Sometimes I will have a margarita or a beer. I always stick with one drink and I don't drink more than once or twice per month. The Bible says that Jesus turned water into wine at a wedding. This shows that it's okay to enjoy your alcohol on occasion, sensibly. Everything in moderation.

Other Foods

Processed foods, frozen foods and already prepared foods can contain chemicals, preservatives, artificial sweeteners, artificial colors and other things that may cause anything from cancer to fetal damage. Organic foods are less likely to have things in them that are not good for you. However, even some organic foods have harmful chemicals. One of the most common food additives used is MSG, which is a preservative and flavor enhancer. MSG is linked to many health problems including headaches, dizziness, heart palpitations, shortness of breath, high blood pressure and hyperactivity.

Many people don't know that MSG goes by many different names, so when you are looking for MSG in foods, you must know all of its names. Here are some of the many names that MSG hides under: natural flavoring, yeast extract, autolyzed yeast extract, hydrolyzed yeast, autolyzed soy, hydrolyzed soy, disodium guanylate, disodium inosinate, caseinate, textured protein, hydrolyzed pea protein and many others. There are 100's of chemicals and additives you have to watch out for. The list can seem overwhelming, but I would like to give you a list of some of the most common toxic substances in the foods you may be eating right now. This list comes from a variety of experts and researchers and is based on many scientific studies done on each of these food additives showing the dangerous health effects of their use. Avoid these whenever possible.

MSG (Monosodium glutamate)
High fructose corn syrup
Transfats

Butylated hydroxyanisole (BHA), BHA and BHT (E320)
Blue #1 and Blue #2 (E133)
Red dye # 3 (also Red #40 – a more current dye) (E124)

Yellow #6 (E110) and Yellow Tartrazine (E102)
Sodium Sulfite (E221)
Sodium Nitrate
Sodium Nitrite

Sulfur dioxide (E220)
Potassium bromate
Sodium chloride (salt – sea or otherwise)

Artificial sweeteners (Aspartame, NutraSweet, Equal, saccharin, Sweet'N Low,
SugarTwin, Acesulfame-K and sucralose (Splenda)
Propyl Gallate

Potassium sorbate
Polysorbate 80
Soy lecithin
Canola Oil
BPA (Bisphenol-A) used to line canned food and also in plastic you store food in.

My list of recommendations for dealing with all of these food chemicals:

Read the labels on everything and try not to buy products with any of the ingredients on the list above. If you don't recognize an ingredient on the label, don't buy the food.

Buy organic foods as much as possible, but read the labels on prepackaged organic foods, because some may still have chemicals.

Prepare and cook fresh food as much as possible and avoid packaged or canned foods as much as possible.

Instead of buying canned vegetables, which have less vitamins and nutrients, go for the frozen organic vegetables instead.

Find brands/companies that never use chemicals, preservatives and additives in their food and stick with those brands.

Grow your own organic fruits and vegetables.

Most store bought mixed-seasoning packets, soy sauce, salad dressings, gravies and sauces are loaded with MSG and other chemicals and preservatives. It is best to make your own seasonings with herbs and sea salt or make your own salad dressings, gravies and sauces. The Food Network, has many recipes for these things as does Allrecipes.com

Since most frozen prepared, packed foods contain added preservatives and chemicals, try not to by frozen foods unless they are 100% organic and say that there are NO preservatives or additives and no artificial flavors/colors added. The Annie's brand is my favorite! If you have to buy non-organic frozen foods, make sure they don't have the additives, preservatives and chemicals.

If you have to sweeten your foods, use stevia or honey.

When you are making breads, pies, cakes, cookies and other baked goods, make them from scratch instead of using the boxed mixes. If you have to use a boxed mix, there are many organic brands of boxed baking mixes. I even found an organic brownie mix that tastes much better than the non-organic brands.

Since organic foods are more expensive than non-organic food, it may be financially difficult for you to buy organic all of the time. If you can't afford organic foods all the time, try to buy organic or fresh foods whenever financially possible. Keep in mind that your health and life are a priceless investment and you may be paying a little more for the food now, but you will possibly avoid doctor visits, hospital stays and premature death.

If money is really tight, think carefully about what you are considering as essential. Your body is a temple and you need to take care of it first.

Vitamins, Herbs and Supplements

In most cases, vitamins, herbs and supplements are good for you, but they can also be harmful. Vitamins, herbs and supplements are not regulated by the FDA, so no one is making sure that what you buy doesn't contain heavy metals, toxins and other things that are bad for your body. Ever hear the phrase, "Too much of a good thing is not always good?" If you take high doses of natural products and vitamins, you may possibly poison yourself or create serious health problems with toxic overdoses. It's important to never take more than the recommended dose of anything, unless your doctor tells you otherwise. There are some vitamins that may be safe in very high doses, but it's better to be safe than sorry, by always checking with a physician who is highly knowledgeable about vitamins and supplements first.

To protect yourself, it is good to check with your doctor before taking any new thing that you are not used to taking and hasn't been prescribed for you. Over the years, many natural supplements have been pulled off the market because they caused illness or death.

Unfortunately, there are many herbs and plants that are highly toxic and poisonous to humans and animals - too many to list in this book. I recommend that you research, investigate and talk with your doctor about any herb you are considering taking. You can find out most info on WebMD.com, and there are other websites that can help you identify dangerous herbs.

Just because an herb works for other people, doesn't mean it will work for you. I mentioned at the beginning of this book that every person's body is unique and what works for you will not work for your neighbor. Please keep this in mind when trying new substances!

Make sure that you always buy vitamins, herbs and supplements from well-known and reputable companies.

Seek out brands that meet GMP standards, have 3rd party testing and guarantee the purity and ingredients are exactly what is listed on the bottle or package. Fish oils, which are very healthy for your heart and blood pressure, have been shown to have high amounts of mercury and carcinogens. The only way to get mercury-free oil is to buy brands like Nordic Naturals and Carlson that have been 3rd party tested to be mercury and toxin free and come from the pristine waters of the North Atlantic and Arctic Oceans.

Another thing to watch out for is supplements and vitamins that have expired or have been open for a long time. It is important that you always use fresh products. Rancid, expired or old products can be toxic and harmful to your body.

The Toxic Effects of Prescription Drugs

The topic of prescription drugs is causing huge arguments in the medical community and amongst the people of this planet. There are some cases where prescription drugs are very necessary, for example if you have a bacterial infection and need antibiotics or you have congestive heart failure or diabetes. If you are currently taking prescription drugs for any health condition, please don't stop taking them just because you are reading this book. Make sure you discuss this with your doctor first.

Unfortunately, there is a dark side to both prescription and over the counter drugs and that is side-effects and death. Every drug on the market has pages of side effects, including death and they even go over the list on TV commercials. There are hundreds and thousands of lawsuits all over the world, against drug companies, because drugs have harmed or killed many people since their inception. The main problem with drugs is that they do not heal or cure any health problem or the root cause of the health problem. Most drugs, with the exception of bacterial infection-killing antibiotics, only mask the symptoms of the health problem. Diabetes medication and insulin do not cure diabetes, they just artificially maintain your blood sugar levels. Heart medications do not reverse or cure heart disease, they only keep you functioning for a little longer – which might be a good-enough result compared to an earlier death. It's up to you. Everyone in my family who died from congestive heart failure (CHF) was on multiple medications that did not cure them. Both my father and father-in-law were taking many different types of medications and both died at ages 78 and 79 from CHF, despite all of the medications.

Drugs are formulated in laboratories and made mostly of chemicals. Since there are no manmade chemicals in existence that are good for the human body, why would we think that drugs would be beneficial? I believe that human beings need to put only natural substances that come from nature into our bodies, not chemicals created in a laboratory.

Over the years, I have experienced bad reactions to drugs and had terrible side effects. What's interesting about that is that the drugs never do for me what they are supposed to do. For example, when I take muscle relaxants for a back ache, they don't relax my muscles, they only make me pass out. When I take pain killers, the pain does not go away. When I took anti-anxiety medicine many years ago, I was still anxious and also suffered multiple side effects. When I took heart medication for an arythmia, I still had the arythmia and had many side effects. The only drugs that seem to work for me personally are antibiotics and certain headache medicines.

The only prescription drugs that I have found to date, that I feel are extremely beneficial to mankind and heal your body from an illness are bacteria-killing antibiotics. What's interesting is that the foundation of antibiotics is nature, not chemicals. In 1928, at St. Mary's Hospital in London England, biologist and bacterial scientist Alexander Fleming discovered penicillin. The story is that Dr. Fleming came back from a vacation and upon examining some colonies of Staphylococcus aureus, he noted that a mold called Penicillium notatum had contaminated his Petri dishes. After carefully placing the dishes under his microscope, he was amazed to find that the mold prevented the normal growth of the Staphylococcus. He waited a few more weeks to confirm his findings. His conclusions was that some factor in the Penicillium mold not only inhibited the growth of the bacteria but, more importantly, might be harnessed to combat infectious diseases. Without antibiotics, many millions of people would die every year from infections.

Unfortunately, doctors have overprescribed antibiotics for decades and given them to our food supply, so now we have an outbreak of many deadly and antibiotic-resistant bacteria like TB and MRSA. I recently noticed that the antibiotic Natamycin is used in everything from parmesan cheese to bread products as a preservative and mold inhibitor. One day I realized that my family had been eating this same antibiotic over and over again in our bread and parmesan cheese. I started to wonder if the reason why my family members and I have had antibiotic resistant illnesses was because we were consuming antibiotics every day in our food. Since I realized that, I have stopped buying any food products containing Natamycin.

The best thing you can do for yourself and your family, is to only take antibiotics when you have a serious bacterial, strep, or other infection. Viruses don't respond to anti-biotics! If you have a virus like a cold or flu, antibiotics will not help and you will need to do other things. There are anti-viral products and supplements you can take to get over a virus faster.

You can also use supplements, herbs and oils that are effective in killing viral infections. Make sure to always check with your doctor before taking anything.

Here is a list of natural substances you can take that have been shown to kill infections. These are all things that are recommended by holistic doctors and are helpful for infections like MRSA that are antibiotic-resistant:

Garlic
Manuka Honey (from New Zealand)
Oil of Oregano
Cayenne Pepper

Grapefruit Seed Extract
Vitamin C
Goldenseal

Colloidal Silver
Oregon Grape

Olive Leaf Extract

Turmeric

Pau D' Arco - Ginger

Before taking any of the things on this list, do some research for yourself on what they are, how much to take and check with your doctor first.

The Impact of Antibiotics, Chemicals and Stress on Your Digestive System

In the previous section, I discussed the problem with overuse of antibiotics. Now I would like to discuss one of the important issues with antibiotics that everyone should know and that is the impact on your digestive system. Antibiotics, along with chemicals, toxins and other stresses kill off the good bacteria in your intestines and create an imbalance in your gut. Unhealthy gut bacteria, or lack of good bacteria, can cause an overgrowth of Candida albicans in the body, which causes yeast infections, sugar cravings and many other health problems. Lack or imbalance of good bacteria in the intestinal track has been linked to autoimmune disorders, Leaky Gut Syndrome, gluten intolerance, food allergies, digestive problems, Irritable Bowel Syndrome, inflammation, viruses and many other problems. I personally used to have several of these problems until I started taking a high quality probiotic. Now my IBS is gone, food allergies are gone, leaky gut syndrome is gone and I am digesting my food better.

According to renowned PBS educator, health and nutrition expert Brenda Watson C.N.C., over 70% of your immune system is in your gut. Brenda Watson also says that there are several other factors besides using antibiotics that can damage our guts and make it hard for the friendly bacteria to thrive:

Microbes like yeast

Parasites we pick up from traveling, swimming in lakes or eating undercooked food.

Overuse of antacids which messes up the pH balance in our gut.

Undigested food – Low stomach acid can cause a problem with digestion of food and undigested food leads to inflammation and leaky gut.

Environmental toxic chemicals

Age – After age 50 our friendly bacteria begins to decline naturally. Because of this, it is most important for seniors to be taking probiotics every day.

It is important for your gut defense system to take a high quality probiotic every day. When you are not on an antibiotic, you should take a high quality probiotics at least one time each day. When you are taking an antibiotic, make sure to take the probiotic a few hours before or afterwards so they do not interfere with each other. You cannot just depend on yogurt for your probiotics because probiotics in yogurt are destroyed by your stomach acid. It is important to take an enteric-coated or delayed release capsule that breaks down in your intestine, not in your stomach. Please note that many probiotics require refrigeration. There are some brands you can buy that are shelf-stable. The shelf stable brands are great for taking on travel. When you buy a good probiotic, here are some of the things you want to look for, according to Brenda Watson:

15+ billion culture count

10+ strains of good bacteria. Since there are between 300 and 1000 strains in the human gut, 10 is a small number. Watson recommends getting both bifidobacterium and lactobacillus strains.

Delayed release, to help make it past the acidic environment of the stomach.

Potency at expiration. A big issue with probiotics is potency when you take it. Better probiotics will tell you on the label how many cultures are guaranteed at product expiration.

Another thing you should be eating or taking every day to help protect your digestive system from the negative impact of antibiotics and also to keep a healthy gut flora and digestive system year round, are organisms called prebiotics. If you are not familiar with prebiotics, they are indigestible food ingredients that stimulate the growth and maintenance of beneficial gut microflora (bacteria). Prebiotics are basically food for your flora. Prebiotics are classified as soluble fiber. The most common prebiotics include: Inulin, Oligofructose, Fructooligosaccharides (FOS), Galactooligosaccharides (GOS), and other Oligosaccharides. Some of the foods that contain prebiotics include: chicory root, Jerusalem artichoke, burdock root, dandelion greens, garlic, leek, onion, bananas, asparagus and some fermented foods like kimchi and sauerkraut.

Some of the benefits of prebiotics include:

Dietary inulin and oligofructose increase fecal bifidobacteria.

Dietary inulin and oligofructose increase magnesium and calcium absorption.

In research studies, prebiotics (inulin, oligofructose, and xylooligosaccharides) exhibited inhibitory effects on precancerous colon lesions in rats. Xylooligosaccharides increased gastrointestinal flora more than inulin and oligofructose, indicating possibly greater effectiveness.

One study showed that an eight week regimen of 4g daily xylooligosaccharides reduced fasting glucose, HbA1c, oxLDL, LDL, and apolipoprotein B levels in Type 2 diabetes patients.
Prebiotics increase the production of short chain fatty acids in the human colon, including beneficial butyric acid.

Galactooligosaccharides improved symptoms in patients with Irritable Bowel Syndrome.
Prebiotics combined with probiotics (called synbiotics) was more effective at gut modulation than either alone.

Chemicals and Toxins in Your Home and Garage

There are thousands of toxic items surrounding us daily in our homes and garages. The paint, insulation, carpeting and wood flooring, and every other part of our home right down to the foundations, are loaded with chemicals. When a new home is built, it takes up to 5 years to outgas all of the chemicals that go into that home. If you move into a home right after it's built, guess who gets to absorb all the outgassing chemicals? You do! Since I am highly sensitive and have many allergies, I made a deal with my husband years ago that we would never buy a house less than 6 years old. I want to minimize my chemical exposure.

Besides all of the toxic chemicals that go into building a home, you bring more toxic chemicals into your home every time you buy furnishings, household cleaners, items for your garage and pesticides and other products for your garden. Everything from your laundry soap to your glass cleaner are toxic. These chemicals also wind up going into ground water and into our lakes, rivers, streams and oceans. Then, we eat the toxic fish from the waters we have polluted and ingest more toxins.

What else do you bring into your home that can possibly make you sick? Consider utensils, plates, cups, pots, pans, storage containers, aluminum foil, plastic bags, plastic wrap and styrofoam. The BPA and other chemicals in plastic containers have been linked to breast cancers, hormonal imbalances and other cancers and illnesses. The Teflon coating on frying pans and other cookware, has been linked to cancer and also proven to kill birds. If you have a pet bird and you cook on Teflon, you have a chance of that bird dying. Their bodies cannot handle that chemical. If Teflon outgassing kills a pet bird, what is it doing to the inside of your body? Another cookware issue is aluminum pots and pans. Aluminum has been linked to Alzheimers Disease and other health problems.

Many of the products we use for our pets are toxic. If you are using chemicals on pets for flea and tick control, you are getting exposed to those as well. Even your pet's shampoo can be toxic. Pet dander, which may not be a chemical, can still act like a toxin because it causes health problems for people with allergies and asthma. In my house, one of the biggest toxins for me is not my cat's dander, but the dust mites in my bedroom. I am highly allergic to dust mites. I have to do things daily to lower my exposure to dust mites. Dust mites may not be a chemical but they are toxic to people who are allergic or have asthma.

Many items in your environment can be toxic even if they are not a chemical or metal. Some non-chemical toxins in your home are mold and fungus. This is more prevalent in damp places like homes close to the ocean and places with high humidity like Washington, Florida or Hawaii. Mold and fungus can make people very sick and also can create allergies and asthma in normally healthy people. I have had a mold and fungus allergy for many years and have to work hard to keep it out of my home. There are some molds that are so toxic that they can send you to the hospital, so it's important to keep mold out of your home. If you suspect you have a mold problem, it is beneficial to contact a company that specializes in mold and fungus removal. If you try to remove the mold yourself, make sure to wear a mask that seals you away from any gas.

There have been many news reports over the last 20 years regarding dangerous chemicals in our homes. Lately there has been controversy over lead and other dangerous metals in dishes and cups from China. I have personally bought lead testing kits to test all of my coffee mugs and dishes that are made in China. Luckily, I only had to throw away a few of them. When you are buying dishes, make sure that you know where they come from and check to see if they are lead free.

Another controversy in home interior industry, has been surrounding granite countertops that leak radon gas into the air. Radon is a very dangerous gas that can be in the soil under your home or stored in rock, like granite. When I had my kitchen remodeled and bought a granite counter top, I also purchased a radon test kit to test my granite and make sure it did not have radon.

Another problem that has appeared in the news, is from people using gas generators or BBQ's inside their home during a power outage or storm. Many people have died from the toxic fumes from doing this. If you are like me and love BBQ food, then you may be disappointed to find out that barbequed foods contain carcinogens that cause cancer. It has to do with the cooking process. In general, overcooking or overheating food is not beneficial. It is important to cook your food long enough to get it up to safe temperature to have killed any bacteria in the meat, but overcooking will cause dangerous carcinogens to be released and also kills the beneficial nutrients in the food. The advice "Everything in moderation" applies to cooking your food as well, so don't undercook or over cook. If you have a problem with this, I recommend investing in a good thermometer and watching lots of cooking shows on the Food Network.

You are in total control over every item that comes into your house. You also have some control over the design and building of your home, if you are custom building a home or doing a remodel. That being said, here are some suggestions for how you can protect yourself and your family from toxic chemicals in your home.

Use a HEPA filter in your vacuum cleaner to get rid of dust, dander and pollen
Put a good quality filter in your home heating system and have it changed regularly.

Have your home duct or ventilation system cleaned regularly.

Do your best to dust mite-proof your home if you or your family members have allergies or asthma. There are many websites that sell special bedding and other supplies to get rid of dust mites.

If you buy a home, try to buy one that is 5 or more years old so the house has time to outgas from the toxic chemicals used to build it.

If you custom build a home, you can use environmentally-safe products that will be better for you and your family.

When you remodel your home or put in new flooring, try using environmentally safe products. There are many new companies providing these, since environmental consciousness is growing on our planet.

If your home is attached to your garage, make sure that the vapors from the chemicals in your garage are not getting into the ventilation system in your home or leaking into your home in other ways. In a perfect world we would all have detached garages that are at least a few yards away from our homes so we don't breathe in gas, oil and other garage chemicals. People who live in apartments have the benefit of having their car far from their living quarters. Unfortunately, most people have their cars close to their home.

When painting, use low VOC (Volatile Organic Compounds) products because VOCs go into the air you breathe as the paint dries. If you use high VOC paints in a baby nursery or child's room, your children are absorbing high levels of toxic chemicals.

When you buy granite or quartz counter tops for your home, make sure to buy types of granite that are guaranteed to not contain radon. If you have granite, you can buy a radon test kit to use on your granite to see if it has deadly radon in it. If you find out your granite has radon, you will want to replace it with something safer.

If you have a fireplace, have your chimney cleaned to protect yourself and your family from creosote coming into your home. Creosote is deadly to breathe in and it causes house fires.

Install carbon monoxide detectors all over your home. Carbon monoxide poisoning is a problem because the gas is odorless so if there is a leak, you won't realize anything is wrong until it's too late.

Replace all your house cleaning chemicals with environmentally-safe ones. There are several brands on the market that are safe for your body and the environment. You can also use lemon juice, grapefruit seed extract, baking soda and vinegar to clean most things.

Replace pesticides with natural bug repellants that are made of herbs and essential oils. Search for the keywords natural bug repellants or environmentally safe pest control on the web.

Replace your Teflon-coated and aluminum cookware, pots and pans with ceramic cookware, stainless steel, glass cookware or cast iron cookware.

The US has regulations that keep lead and other toxic metals out of our kitchen ware. To protect your family from household goods like cups, plates and silverware that contain lead and other dangerous metals, make sure to buy reputable brands that are known to be safe. Stick with lead-free, microwave and dishwasher-safe goods. If you have things manufactured outside of the United States, consider buying a lead test kit to use on one of each of the sets you own to make sure they are safe. These test kits are very inexpensive and will save your health.

Since plastic containers and plastic bags have BPA and other chemicals, try to store your food and leftovers in class or ceramic containers. If you have to store your food in plastic, buy BPA-free plastic containers and BPA free bags. They are available at most grocery stores.

Instead of using aluminum wrap and plastic wrap, use glass and ceramic with lids or BPA free plastic containers instead of aluminum and plastic whenever possible. Glass and ceramic containers come in many sizes these days. I bought some perfect sandwich sized glass containers with BPA free lids for my husband and kids to take to work and school. The pleasant side benefit of using the glass or ceramic storage containers is that you save money while you keep the disposable plastic and aluminum out of the environment.

Mercury Toxicity in Our Food and Environment

Of all of the negative things our bodies and brains are bombarded with daily, Mercury is probably the most dangerous toxin of all. Methylmercury [CH3Hg] is the most toxic form. It affects the immune system, alters genetic and enzyme systems, and damages the nervous system, including coordination and the senses of touch, taste, and sight.

Methylmercury is most damaging to developing embryos in pregnant women, birds and animals. Exposure to methylmercury is usually by ingestion, and it is absorbed more readily and excreted more slowly than other forms of mercury. Elemental mercury, Hg(0), the form released from broken thermometers, causes tremors, gingivitis, and excitability when vapors are inhaled over a long period of time. Mercury can get stored in your brain and will stay there causing health problems and even death, until you detox it out of your body.

People are exposed to methylmercury by eating contaminated fish and wildlife that are at the top of aquatic food chains. Women who eat a large amount of seafood like tuna, which is very high in mercury, are exposing their future children to high levels of the toxin.
According to a report on the toxicological effects of methylmercury in 2000 by the National Research Council, more than 60,000 children are born each year at risk for adverse neurodevelopmental effects due to in-utero exposure to methylmercury. The
Environmental Protection Agency, presented a report to Congress in 1997 that concluded mercury may pose a risk to some adults and wildlife populations that consume large amounts of fish that is contaminated by mercury. The types of fish that have the highest amounts of mercury are the large top of the food chain fish like shark, tuna, swordfish and others. Much of the fish these days also contain PCBs and other toxic chemicals. Farmed fish have the highest content on non-mercury toxins.

If you are a fish lover like me, you are probably wondering what types of fish are safe to eat, with all the mercury and chemicals in fish. According to http://www.seafoodwatch.org, the following fish are the best choices:

Abalone
Arctic Char (farmed)

Barramundi (US & Vietnam farmed)
Bass: Striped (US hook and line, farmed)

Catfish (US)
Clams, Mussels & Oysters
Cod: Pacific (AK)
Lobster: Spiny (Mexico)

Prawn: Spot (AK & Canada)
Rockfish (CA, OR & WA)
Sablefish/Black Cod (AK)
Salmon (AK & New Zealand)

Sanddab (CA, OR & WA)
Sardines: Pacific (Canada & US)
Scallops (farmed)
Seaweed (farmed)

Shrimp (AK wild, US farmed)
Tilapia (Ecuador & US)
Trout: Rainbow (US farmed)

Tuna: Albacore (Pacific troll, pole and line)
Tuna: Skipjack (Pacific troll, pole and line)

The www.seafoodwatch.org website also has suggestions for seafood to avoid.

Although fish is a major source for mercury, there is one other source of mercury that an even bigger problem than fish and that is the dentist's office. If you have ever had a cavity filled in your lifetime with an amalgam (silver) filling, you have toxic levels of mercury that are leaching into your body daily. Many doctors have stopped using the amalgam fillings and switched to porcelain and other types, but there are still millions of people walking around with toxic mercury amalgam fillings in their mouths. Furthermore, every time a dentist and their staff remove these fillings, the dentist and staff are breathing in the dust and vapors from the mercury. It is also going into the air of the office and into the environment. A century ago, mercury was used in the felting process to manufacture hats. Hat makers would go crazy - Mad Hatters syndrome - which is where the idea for the character in Alice in Wonderland came from.

There is a theory that many dentists suffer from Mad Hatter's Syndrome, due to their ingesting mercury in their office every day. This would explain why dentists have the highest rate of suicide of any profession. The fillings in your mouth leach mercury into your body, non-stop until you have them removed. When you have amalgam fillings removed from your mouth, large amounts of the mercury can enter your body at one time, if you do not have a dentist who is an expert at removing amalgam fillings. It is important to have a good dentist who can use measures to protect you when he/she removes your amalgam fillings. Keep in mind that there are no guarantees. Even if a doctor tries to use safe methods for removal, it doesn't guarantee you will not ingest mercury. Over time, mercury builds up in your body and does not come out until you use measures to remove it via detox.

Mercury also shows up in water, food, dishes, lightbulbs and many other places in our environment. There is only one thing you can do about all the mercury in our environment and that is to do a regular detox. In the last section of this chapter, I will discuss detoxification of chemicals, heavy metals and toxins.

The Real Cost of Cosmetics and Personal Care

The cosmetics and personal care products industries are multi-billion dollar industries. Companies are getting rich from our desire to smell good, look good and take care of ourselves. The financial cost of buying these products for you and for your family is very high, but the price you are paying with your health is even higher. Your skin is the largest organ on your body and everything you put on your skin goes into your blood stream and is carried to every organ and cell in your body. That is why there are many drugs on the market that are in the form of a patch that you place on your skin. Medication can go right into your blood stream through your skin. So, what do you think happens when you put chemicals or toxins on your skin?

Unfortunately, many of the cosmetics and personal care products you are using every day are full of chemicals, toxins and heavy metals. These substances are in toothpaste, mouthwash, makeup, perfumes, lotions, soaps, ointment, shampoo, other hair care products and many other personal care items. Most underarm deodorants are loaded with aluminum, which has been linked to Alzheimer's disease. There are also other chemicals added to underarm deodorants.

A report that appeared in Forbes magazine in 2012, reported that an FDA investigation found imported skin creams that contain toxic levels of mercury and other heavy metals. The list of dangerous skin creams is long but there were no American made products on the list. Buy American! Instead the list of dangerous cosmetics was completely made of foreign cosmetics that came from the Latino market, Asia and the Middle East. The FDA also tested hundreds of lipsticks, following an alert issued by the Campaign for Safe Cosmetics. Two consecutive FDA investigations found that there was lead in 100 percent of the lipsticks tested – and the amounts they found are not small! The first FDA test revealed lead levels up to 3.06 ppm (parts per million).

A second FDA test, published in Cosmetic Science in 2012, found lead levels up to 7.19 ppm. What is really upsetting to me is that the brands that tested positive for lead levels are brands I have been using for many years. The list included L'Oreal, Revlon, Avon, and Cover Girl and also included high-end lipstick like MAC and Dior. Five of the ten most contaminated lipsticks were manufactured by L'Oreal USA. Even more disturbing is that even some "natural" brands like Burt's Bees were on the list and tested positive for a fair amount of lead. There is no safe level for lead.

I have been researching personal care items and cosmetics for years to find ones that are safe for myself and my family and what I have found is that most of the items sold in the stores are full of heavy metals, chemicals and toxic substances. Even items like toothpaste and mouthwash are loaded with chemicals that you should not use. Trying to look beautiful and smell good has become a deadly experience. Everything you put into your mouth or on your skin has the potential to help you or harm you. It's up to you to take control of your life and health by voting with your dollars. T

The best way to protect yourself and your family from these toxic chemicals in cosmetics and personal care items is to buy brands that contain 100% naturally-sourced and even organic ingredients that you know are safe to use. There are many brands you can buy at Whole Foods Markets and other natural foods/supplement stores that are safe to use. Make sure to buy items that have been safety tested for purity. One natural cosmetic brand that I use for lipstick and other makeup is 100% Pure. All of their lipstick is made with food-grade ingredients.

Make sure to read the labels on everything you buy and look out for names of toxic ingredients. According to www.safecosmetics.org, some of the important chemicals that you should watch out for in cosmetic products because they can cause everything from cancer to reproductive problems includes:

1,4-Dioxane   - Benzophene and related compounds
Butylated compounds - Carbon Black

Coal Tar	- Fragrance
Homosalate	- Hydraquinone
Lead	- Mica
Nail Polish Removers	- Octinoxate
Polyacrylamide	- Polytetrafluoroethylene (PTFE, AKA Teflon)
Octinoxate	- Polyacrylamide
P- Phenylendiamine	- Parabens
Phthalates	- Quaternium – 15
Resorcinol	- Retinol and Retinol compounds
Synthetic Musks	- Talc
Titanium Dioxide	- Toluene
Triclosan	- Sulfates

- Ethanolamine compounds (MEA, DEA, TEA and others)
- Formaldehyde and Formaldehyde releasing preservatives
- Nitrosamines (diethanolamine (DEA) and triethanolamine (TEA))

Your Clothing May be Killing You

Have you ever purchased new clothing and noticed it has stinky smell? Well, I certainly have. In fact, I have washed new clothes and the smell remained after washing, so I had to return the offensive clothing. If your clothes have a funny smell when you purchase them, it is a red flag that they are full of chemicals. These nasty chemicals enter into the garment during the manufacturing process and can be in either natural or synthetic clothing.

According to an article in Total Health Magazine, there are over 8,000 synthetic chemicals in your clothing yet consumers believe that synthetic fibers are safe. Unfortunately, these synthetic fibers and other chemicals in clothing have been causing everything from skin disorders and infertility to respiratory diseases and cancer in humans. The more synthetic clothing you wear, the greater your risk of absorbing toxic chemicals that will make you sick.

I mentioned in the previous section on cosmetics that our skin is the largest organ in the body and everything you put on your skin goes right into your blood stream and organs. Well, clothing is something you put on your skin, right? So you need to be careful with the types of clothing you are buying.

Much of the clothing today is made of petrochemical fibers that restrict and suffocate your skin, preventing toxins from releasing from your body. Many health experts are clueless about the fact that synthetic fabrics are full of chemicals and dyes that cannot be washed out, making them a potential health hazard. Most synthetic fabrics, from towels to dress shirts and bed linens, are treated with chemicals during and after processing. These chemicals not only leach into the environment, impacting groundwater, wildlife, air and soil, but they also may be absorbed or inhaled directly.

Do you ever buy "Wrinkle free" or "Wrinkle resistant" clothes? Well, unfortunately they are made with deadly perfluorinated chemicals (PFCs), which include the non-stick additive Teflon. Also, most clothing labeled "no-iron" contains PFCs. If you have allergies or asthma, you will be more sensitive to the chemicals in clothing and you especially need to watch out for all of the chemicals in bedding and sheets. Many people all over the world are having allergic reactions to synthetic fibers and chemicals that are in their bedding, clothing, car interiors, exercise/athletic clothing, mattresses, hats and etc. To manage chemical stress you must be on the lookout for the following fabric finishes when buying things:

Easy Care, wrinkle-free, shrinkage-free—these garments release formaldehyde

Water Repellent - Fluoropolymers (as in Teflon) are used to repel oil and water

Flame Retardants - Lab studies have shown that flame retardants (PBDEs) can cause a slew of health issues: thyroid problems, brain damage, ADHD symptoms, fertility problems and even cancer.

Bacterial and Fungicidal Chemicals—Triclosan and nano-particles are used for these purposes; they are dangerous neurotoxins and irritants. Fabrics containing Formaldehyde arc linked to a 30 percent increase in lung cancer, skin/lung irritation and contact dermatitis

Anti-cling, anti-static, anti-shrink
Waterproof
Perspiration-proof

Moth-proof and mildew resistant
Chlorine resistant
Disperse Dyes (especially dark blue, brown and black synthetic clothing). According to studies Disperse Blue # 1 is classified as a human carcinogen due to high malignant tumor levels in lab animals.

The chemicals in clothing cause such a problem that the U.S. Marine Corps prohibits troops in Iraq from wearing synthetic clothing while off base. With all of this disturbing information, I am sure you are wondering what you can do about it. My best advice is to choose natural fibers and if possible organic fabrics. Natural fibers include: cotton, flax, hemp, silk, wool, alpaca, angora, camel, cashmere, mohair and ramie. When you buy new clothes, wash them well before wearing them for the first time. The same goes with bedding. Using vinegar and baking soda in the wash will help to remove some of the chemicals used during production. Unfortunately, there are many chemicals you cannot remove during washing if you buy synthetic clothing. Try to minimize the amount of synthetic-fabric clothing and shoes that you buy.

Managing Chemical Stress by Detoxing Your Body

I obviously covered a lot of scary territory in this chapter. If you are feeling a little scared or worried right now about all of the toxic chemicals in our world, don't let fear and worry make you sick. Instead, take charge of your health by using the advice I have given you in each section and do a regular detox on your body to get all of the chemicals, heavy metals and other toxins out. Although we don't have control over all of our chemical exposure, there are still things we can do to prevent it and also heal and remove it from our bodies and brains. Detoxing is your biggest tool for chemical, toxin and heavy metal defense. Unfortunately, there are many detox products on the market that can make you sick and give you nasty side effects.

I personally tried to use detox products many years ago and had horrible side effects, a healing crisis and other issues. What I have learned is that the human body is delicate and we need to treat it with care. There are many gentle ways to detox your body without having side effects like nausea, headaches and other problems.

Here is my list of simple and healthy ways to detox your body to manage chemical stress. Before starting any of these suggestions, please check with your doctor first.

Drink warm water with juice from a fresh squeezed lemon first thing in the morning. This trick has been used in China and other places in the world for thousands of years. The lemon juice and water works on your liver and kidneys to get rid of toxins that way.

Do daily activities that cause your body to sweat. When you sweat, you excrete toxins out of your skin. Some of the best ways to do this are exercise, hot shower, sit in a hot tub or Jacuzzi or sit in a dry sauna or steam room.

Drink a tablespoon of Braggs Apple Cider Vinegar in water 1 to 3 times a day right before a meal. Not only does this help with detox, but also helps your digestion and overall health.

Get rid of heavy metals like mercury and lead by eating cilantro and parsley every day. You can just eat these fresh in your salad or food or you can cook them or juice them. Other herbs and spices that are helpful for detoxification are garlic, cinnamon, oregano, turmeric, cumin, fenugreek, ginger, fennel, cayenne pepper, black pepper, clove and rosemary.

Try using NCD2 (Natural Cellular Defence) by Waiora. This is made out of a zeolite crystal that has been used in China for thousands of years for detoxing. Zeolite crystal attaches itself to heavy metals like mercury and lead as well as other toxins and gently sweeps them out of the body through your urine or feces. I have been using this product for year and got rid of several toxin- caused fibroid tumors with this stuff. I have seen it work miracles on people with stage 4 cancers. This product is gentle enough to give to dogs and babies. The only downside is you must drink a lot of water when you take it or you can get dehydrated. The product uses water to pull the bad stuff out of your body.

Use herbs like dandelion root, burdock root, green tea and milk thistle for detoxing your liver and gallbladder. Milk Thistle is beneficial but must be used with caution. You should only use it a few times a year and only for a one week period. Using this herb daily and for extended periods of time can cause damage to your liver and other problems. Some people may be allergic to dandelion so be careful with it; work with your doctor on a safe strategy.

An Ayurvedic remedy that has been used for detox for thousands of years is mung beans. These mighty beans detox your body by absorbing toxic residue from the intestinal walls.

Dry brush your skin.

Use detox foot spas.

Try juicing or smoothies. Some people go on a juice fast for a week, which can do a great job of detoxing your body. I cannot do fasts because my body doesn't like this, but if you are someone who can tolerate fasting, then you may want to try it.

Drink 6 to 8 glasses of water daily.

Take vitamin C, which helps the body produce glutathione, which is a liver compound that drives away toxins. You can also take L-glutamine and other supplements that stimulate your body to make glutathione.

When you start a detox program, listen to your body. If you have negative symptoms like headache or nausea while you are detoxing, either lower the dose of what you are taking or stop taking it. Most of the items I list can be used daily and indefinitely without any side effects, but things like herbs (milk thistle, dandelion and burdock root) should only be used for short periods of time and temporarily. Please make sure to tell your doctor that you are starting a regular detox regimen and get the best advice for your particular situation. Make sure to go easy on yourself. If you are wondering how you will know if you have detoxed all of the chemicals, metals and toxins out your body, there are only two ways to find that out:

You can get blood and hair tests before you a start a detox and retake the tests three months later to see the results. This gives you the most exact data.

You can pay attention to your health and symptoms before and after doing the detox. Usually people who have a lot of chemicals, metals and toxins in their body have health problems. Sometimes they even have major problems like cancer.

After you have been using detox products for one month, you should notice your negative health symptoms going away and you should be feeling better. Each month that goes by, you will notice more and more improvements in your health. Everyone has a different result going through detox, but here are some of the many positive improvements and results that my clients have received by detoxing:

Allergies have gone away
Tumors have shrunk or gone
Skin has cleared up
Chronic headaches have gone away
Brain fog is gone (mercury and other heavy metals, as well as candida, can cause brain fog)
Sleeping better
Improvement in energy levels - Hormones are more balanced
Weight loss (for people who were overweight due to toxic chemicals impacting their thyroid)
Depression or anxiety has gone away
Blood pressure has regulated
Blood sugar has improved

I hope that you notice every positive change as you use this information to make changes in your life. The purpose of this chapter has been to inform you of the impact that toxins and bad chemicals can have on your body. If this information has been too technical or too much to absorb, you owe it to yourself to spend some time doing research on the subject. I have been avidly researching the subject most of my life,

248 | K I M B E R L Y   P A L M

because I want to stay healthy and keep everyone else healthy too. There is so much information in the world about this subject that I was only able to touch on a small amount. The activities on the next page will give you a nice start to protecting yourself and your family.

Activities for Managing Chemical Stress

Spend a day going through your house and replacing all of your cleaning chemicals with environmentally-safe products.

Using the information from this chapter, research a few Natural Antiviral and Antibacterial products that you would like to try out when and if you are sick, check with your physician to make sure they are okay for you and then purchase them.

If you are not taking a good probiotic and prebiotic right now, research a few high quality brands of pro- and prebiotics, choose what you prefer and start taking them daily. See my section with Brenda Watson's recommendation for picking out a good probiotic first.

Each time you buy a cosmetic, skin care or personal care item, buy a natural and organic product to replace your old toxic brand. You may choose to replace all of your toxic personal care products with natural products right away. First, do some research to find the best brands that have been tested for safety.

When you shop for clothing, shoes and bedding, make sure to look for natural fabrics and organic fabrics.

CHAPTER 5
ENVIRONMENT STRESS

W hen you say the word "environment," most people think of trees, water and weather, but these are just a small part of your total environment! The entire environment includes everything that is surrounding you and going on around you, wherever you are at the time. This includes your home, your work, traveling, airports, concerts, football games, amusement parks, your car, friends' houses, walking down the street, the local bar, shopping malls, the park, school, the doctor's office, and every public place in between. Since I don't want to write a 20,000 page book – and you don't want to read one! - I will not be covering every type of environment stress in this book. Instead, I am choosing to cover the most important categories: Home Stress, Work Stress, Public Places and Driving Stress. I will briefly discuss each of these and give you some tips and information on how you can manage Environment Stress.

Stress at home

Every person on earth experiences stress in their home environment. In most cases, this stress can be prevented and managed. There are some incidents where you will not be able to prevent stress at home, but you can manage the way you react to the stress and save your body, mind and spirit from the effects of the stress.

In this section we will discuss what creates stress at home and give you some tips for managing your home stress. First, here is a list of some of the many issues that could create stress at home. See how many of these you identify with.

Lack of money to live comfortably
Paying bills and maintaining your finances and bank accounts □
Unhealthy work-life balance

Poor time management skills (not enough time in the day)
Relationship issues
Rude neighbors

Poor lighting
Temperature in the home is too hot or too cold
Lack of privacy

Noisy environment
Mold, fungus and other allergens in your home
Disorganization and clutter

Living somewhere that you do not like
Living somewhere that is less nice than you like
Hoarding

Cigarette Smoke
Dirty or unhealthy living conditions
Living too far from your place of work (long commute)

House and yard maintenance
Appliances (maintaining them and fixing them when they break) □
Landlord issues if you rent or lease

Financial security and financial worries
Vehicles and maintenance of them
Caring for elderly family members

People living or staying with you temporarily
Room mates
Lack of help with chores around your house

Chores
Keeping food in the cupboard or fridge
Maintaining supplies of life necessities

Hosting parties and meetings at your home
Keeping the house clean
Repairing things, other than the appliances already listed

How many of these items apply to you? Most of my coaching clients would check off almost every one of them. The good news is that you have control over most of these things! For the issues you do not have control over, you can learn skills to manage them and change the way you react to and perceive the people, things, events and situations.

Did you happen to notice that the first few items on the list applied to money? That is because every study ever done on stress lists money as being the number one cause of stress for most people, with relationships and career in the second and third slots.

So now I would like to give you a few basic tips for managing stress at home. I recommend that you utilize the tips that resonate with you and also get some help to deal with the rest of your home stress. I also recommend that you read books, research and/or take some classes to help you. You have to learn how to manage your home stress if you want to live a happy and healthy life.

Money and Finances

If you are stressed over money, then here are some options:

Clear away any blocks or limiting beliefs that are preventing you from receiving money/ abundance (Some people have a poverty mindset that they inherited from family, was learned while growing up or there are some blocks.)

Create, attract and manifest abundance, by changing your thoughts, beliefs and developing a healthy spiritual relationship with money.

Practice gratitude daily to start attracting more abundance.

Reign in your spending. Stop buying things you don't really need until you have enough money to spend on extras. Create healthy priorities around spending money. (see below) Stop your worrying over money and learn how to practice mindfulness (present moment awareness) and the other emotional stress techniques listed in Chapter 3.

Get advice from an expert (financial planner, tax advisor, CPA, church financial consultant or other financial expert.)

Make a spending plan, budget or financial investment plan and stick to it. Start putting away money for retirement, so you don't have to rely on Social Security or a family member for all of your support when you are ready to stop earning. Pray and turn your worries over to God, your angels and guides, and the universe and ask them for help and guidance. You can also call upon the angel of abundance and prosperity to help you.

If you do everything on this list, you are more likely to increase your financial abundance and decrease your stress around money. Most people in this world are addicted to materialism and spend money on all sorts of items they don't really need. Some people spend a lot of their money when they are emotionally stressed, as a way of making themselves feel better. There are people who are addicted to shopping and have Obsessive Compulsive Disorder, which drives them into bankruptcy. If you think you may have a shopping addiction, it is urgent for you to get some help from a mental health therapist. If you continue on this way, it could ruin your life.

If you are someone who is in a financial position where you do not have as much money as you need or would like to have, then the answer is simple: Stop buying stuff! You don't need to have the newest X-Box or latest cell phone model. In fact you don't need any of those things at all. The problem with people in the United States and other First World countries is that they go out and spend tons of money on things they don't really need and use credit to live beyond their current means. My parents, who were poor and financially ignorant, spent their money like water, lived beyond their means and thus remained stuck their entire lives. They wasted money on cigarettes, designer clothes, apartments in expensive neighborhoods and other things that they couldn't really afford. They died broke with thousands of dollars in credit card debt and outstanding loans, the proverbial champagne taste on a beer budget.

I learned from their bad lessons and have never lived the way they did. Instead, I created my own financial/money rules that I live by every day. Because I have worked hard to make better choices than my parents did with my money, I have a comfortable life and money to spend as well as money put away for my retirement. Here is my list of money rules that help me to manage money stress. If this resonates with you, then please use these rules to improve your own life.

Practice gratitude every day. Gratitude is an abundance magnate. Follow my own manifesting techniques that I teach my coaching clients. (I have created an entire manifesting program for people called, Mind Power for Success™) I have developed a good spiritual relationship with money and follow the spiritual principles of money (many people don't have this and that is why they lack money).

I only buy what I need to survive and then spend money on other things. (I have clear priorities.)

I always plan ahead. If I want to go on a vacation, I start saving up for it a year or more in advance. If I want to buy things that are beyond my essential needs, I only buy extra items or services (like spa memberships or concert tickets) when I have enough money in the bank to completely pay for it, without having to have a balance on my credit card. I use credit cards only for collecting points or miles and pay off my balance in full each month. I never want to incur an interest payment or fee.

I keep a monthly spending plan and track all of my spending.
I have a great financial planner, good accountant and my husband and I spend time researching on how to invest our money.
I protect myself and my family by having insurance for everything important (house, cars, health, dental, vision, life, disability and etc.)

I pray daily and ask for guidance.
I donate money to charities whenever possible because giving not only makes me feel happy that I helped people, but it is also true that unselfish giving creates a strong abundance magnet.

Your Home Environment

When you are at home, there are thousands of people, things and events that could possibly cause stress. The first key to managing stress at home is to create a peaceful environment. The opposite of stress is peace and like I taught you in chapter 3, you want to focus on what you want, not on what you don't want. Creating a peace filled home does take some work and effort. You cannot wave a magic wand to create peace, however if you learn some new things and make some changes you can create what you want. I will be sharing some tips with you now on how to start creating your peace-filled home. This is only a beginning to start you out in the right direction, since there are book loads of info on this subject. You may already know some of this, intellectually, and just need encouragement to take action.

Create a peaceful oasis in your home by using soothing paint colors on your home inside and out. Soothing colors include pastels, blues, greens, soft pinks, soft peach, yellows and greys.

Keep live plants in your home. Studies show that live plants boost your immune system, deter illness, help you breathe better, clean the air and help you work better.

Play soft music whenever you feel tired, come home from work, or feel stressed in general.

Use a diffuser or candles for aromatherapy with soothing fragrances like lavender. If you have family or others living with you, have a dedicated room in your home where you can escape for quiet time.

If you work at an outside job, make sure to let your family or roommates know that you need some down time before interacting with them when you first arrive home; take as long as you need in your quiet space to chill out before you deal with the domestic environment. If you are unable to do this, sit on your porch, patio or in your backyard for a little while so you can transition from work to home.
You can also use a hot shower or bubble bath to relax.

Keep your home and garage clean and organized. Clutter causes stress. Hording (the inability to throw things away) is such an epidemic that they have created reality TV shows about it. If you have clutter in your home, your health will be affected and your mind will be cluttered as well. The impact on your health from clutter is everything from allergies and respiratory problems to other health problems. If you have an inability to throw things away, I urge you to get help from a mental health therapist or counselor as soon as possible, because the tendency is unhealthy.

If you are unable to clean your home due to physical limitations, please have family, friends, neighbors or a cleaning service company help you out.

Maintain and take care of your home and appliances to prevent future problems and break downs, leaky roof, peeling paint and other signs of neglect. When things break down, it causes stress. You can avoid some of this stress with prevention. When things do break down, change the way you perceive them. They are not problems, they are temporary speed-bumps in your road of life and sometimes they are just learning lessons. If you look at the things going on in your home in a more positive light, you will not have stress.

Buy insurance for your home, automobiles and your health and life. Lack of insurance can cause much stress in your future. I have known many people who didn't have home insurance and then a fire takes their home away. Imagine the stress you have when you don't prepare and protect yourself.

Create healthy relationships with friends, family, roommates and neighbors. Eliminate any toxic relationships before they kill you. You cannot change other people but you can change yourself, and you can manage how you react or overreact to other people's bad behavior. Get relationship counseling, if you need to or just go talk to someone. It will be cheaper than the illness and hospital bills you will receive by staying in unhealthy relationships.

Make sure the temperature in your home is set at a comfortable level. Keep your home well-heated in the winter time and properly cooled in the summer. Proper insulation is very helpful for this. If you do not have air conditioning, invest in a few good fans. You can also buy a small inexpensive room air conditioner that fits in a window.

Avoid eye strain by placing proper lighting throughout your home. Use soft lighting right before bedtime so you can go to sleep easier. Bright lights stimulate your brain and keep you awake.

Create a healthy work-life balance. When you come home from work, leave your problems at the door. Don't bring work home with you and don't discuss it and think about it while you are at home.

Learn how to manage time while you are home. Wouldn't it be great to have time for yourself and time to do what you love? Well, you can have plenty of time if you learn how. Time management is the first skill I work on with all of my coaching clients, so they are freed up to do the life-changing homework I give to them.

Noisy environments are harmful to your hearing and your mental health. Work towards keeping the noise down in your home. Play TV and music loud enough to hear but not too loud. Ask family members to keep their voices down. If neighbors are using loud equipment (repairs or construction, for example), keep your windows closed. Constant exposure to loud noises not only rattles your nerves and causes anger and anxiety but also destroys your hearing. Invest in some ear plugs if you have to. I spent many years as a young ignorant teenager listening to loud music and going to clubs and concerts. As a result, I have tinnitus and have lost hearing in my right ear. I cannot urge you enough to protect your hearing now.

If you have mold and fungus in your home, take efforts to get rid of it as quickly as possible. Mold and fungus are very harmful to your health.

If you smoke cigarettes, you need to quit. Not only do cigarettes waste your money, cause cancers and lung problems, but it also harms everyone who breathes in the second-hand smoke. If you do not smoke but someone you live with does, ask them to smoke outside only, so you don't have health problems as a result of their addiction. When smoker friends come to visit, ask them to take their cigarettes outside. My parents and other family members smoked around me during my entire childhood. As a result, I developed asthma. Many people who have worked in night clubs, casinos or other smoked filled jobs have died from lung cancer as a result of breathing in 2nd hand smoke. Please have respect for the health of other people who don't smoke, by not smoking around them.

If maintaining a yard is stressful, you have some choices: move to a place that doesn't have a yard; hire someone to take care of your yard for you; have someone else in your family help out; have a neighbor help out, or create a very low maintenance yard with bark, rock and similar choices.

Get everyone in your family to pitch in doing the chores. You can pay your kids an allowance to contribute. If you have a roommate, make sure they do their share of the chores. If you have to do all of the chores in your home, it will cause you to be resentful of your family or roommates and cause relationship issues.

If you or other family members have allergies, use an electric air filter, vacuum with a HEPA filter regularly and buy dust mite covers for all your mattresses and pillows. There are many websites that have tips for reducing allergens in your home. It's important to keep on top of this because allergies are stressful and can make you very sick. Refer to chapter 4 where I originally mentioned this.

Stress in the Workplace

I am not surprised that the World Health Organization says that employers in the United States lose $300 billion a year because of employee stress. Many companies in the world have caused their own problems by doing everything from creating a hostile work environment to not paying their employees enough money or providing good benefits, fostering negative competition, unfair promotion, lack of positive feedback and praise, too much overtime hours, high and unfair expectations and other negative issues that create stress for employees.

If you are in a career or business that you do not like and you spend every day trading your time for a paycheck, you are always going to be unhappy. The key to being happy in your career or business is to be fully living your purpose, love what you are doing, believe that you are making a difference in the world and/or you are doing something that you enjoy and are talented at.

Other keys to job happiness include feeling appreciated, being respected and receiving regular positive feedback. When you are trading time for money in a job you don't like, there will always be stress. Unfortunately, even when you are living your purpose, you are cannot be fully protected from all stress. You can still have some stress, even when you are living your purpose. The difference is that you will be willing to put up with much more, be more patient, have a more positive attitude and you will deal with stress better than if you were not living your purpose.

If you are like most of the human race and have a job you don't like, there are only 3 things you can do:

1. Quit your job and get another one
2. Retire
3. Stay in your job, deal with it and learn some skills to make your job and life less stressful and more enjoyable.

If you are in a job that makes you unhappy and causes stress, the longer you stay in that job the higher your risk is for illness and shorter life. Remember that 98% of illness is caused by stress! If you truly love and respect yourself, you owe it to yourself to get out of situations that are making you sick. Please do not just quit your job because of this book. Make sure that you stay in your job, while looking for another job or maybe business opportunity at the same time. Do not quit your job until you have a new job in place and you are financially stable.

Remember that money is the number one cause of stress? If you are married and your spouse can and wants to support you while you are looking for a new job, then you may choose to leave your stress filled job before it kills you. However, it is always easier to find a new job when you already have one. You are more attractive to prospective employers when you are employed. When employers look at people who have been unemployed for more than three months, they become hesitant and question why you are out of work. I have always had tons of job offers while I was already employed and when I was unemployed it was much harder to find a job.

If you are like the millions of people who are experiencing stress at work, I am going to share with you some information that will help you to have a better work experience.

First, let's talk about some of the many issues in the workplace that cause people unhappiness and stress. Please read carefully through this list and see how many of these pertain to you.

You don't like your job
Long work commute or traffic
Long work hours with too much overtime

Difficult relationships with co-workers
Difficult relationship with boss or employees
Competition

Personality clashes
Lack of cooperation, participation and teamwork
Co-workers with big egos

Lack of support from bosses or coworkers
Lack of support from your employees
Feeling unappreciated or disrespected

Underpaid and overworked
The temperature in your workplace is too hot or too cold
Experiencing neck, eye and back strain from computers or other work you do

Your work area is too small
Unhealthy conditions

Noise level
Inadequate benefits
The job is too difficult
Not living your purpose in your current career

Not feeling connected to what you do for a living
Meeting deadlines
High expectations

Costly mistakes
Accidents and injuries
Having to do other people's work for them

Too much responsibility
Lack of training or learning curve
You are trying to please everyone

Not getting promotions or a co-worker is promoted into a position you
wanted and worked harder for.
Upper management problems
Corporate financial struggles, meeting budgets

Extensive paperwork, contracts, or government bureaucracy
Legal problems

Difficulty running a business
Trying to run your own business without enough business or
marketing skills
And many more reasons why your job gives you stress......

How many of the items on this list were you able to check off? If you checked off one to 3 of the items on the list, then you are experiencing some workplace stress and need to either prevent it, reduce it, delete it or manage it if you want to be happy and healthy. If you checked off several items, then you have a large amount of workplace stress. There will always be some things at work that you cannot prevent, but you can manage the aftereffects. When I do corporate stress training for employees, I sometimes have to spend an entire day or many days over the course of 6 months, teaching people how to manage their work stress.

As in in the other chapters of this book, you will be getting some basic ideas and then you will need to do the rest by working with a coach, taking classes or reading and learning.

Let's talk about some basic ideas for managing your environment stress at work.

Relationships at Work

Relationships at work can be very stressful for most people. You may have rude or competitive coworkers or you may have a boss who treats you badly, overworks you or does not appreciate you. Many people feel unappreciated by their employers. The biggest cause of workplace drama (sometimes trauma) comes under the heading of ego. Some people just have a belief that they are better or superior to everyone else. Others have issues with pride, have low self-esteem, too much confidence (they are know-it-alls) or have a competitive personality. These are just some examples of how ego can rule your co-workers, bosses and employees.

The other problem you have to deal with in the workplace is other peoples' wrong beliefs or bad attitudes. Some people are just mean and seem like they were born in Grinchville. That's right, the Grinch is not just someone who comes out at Christmas time. Some of your co-workers may be the Grinch every day. Competitive people do more harm to a business or organization than good. When co-workers compete it creates a negative environment where people are not motivated to be productive. The best strategy is always team work. When everyone works towards the same goal in the company or organization, then there will be success. Managers and bosses who foster teamwork in their organization will have higher rates of achieving their goals than when a competitive environment exists. The attitude some people take is, "Well Sally's going to get all of the sales anyways so why should I bother?" When the workplace is fun, challenging and supportive, more productive things get done and everyone wins.

Savvy employers create a pay and reward system that encourages teamwork and also a system that helps you compete against yourself. In other words, you beat your own records to get rewarded. This gets rid of any hostility and envy between employees and gives you a challenge to work for.

Unfortunately, you cannot change other people. You can only change yourself by changing your attitude and perceptions, changing your behavior, creating healthy boundaries, improving your confidence and self-esteem, empowering yourself, learning effective communication skills, being respectful to others and working to create peaceful relationships. Everywhere I have worked, there has always been at least one person who I did not get along with well. The truth is that we can't have deep rapport with everyone, but we can do our best to be kind, respectful and compassionate to others so we have a better chance at healthy relationships at work.

Here are some easy tips for improving relationships at work by changing your own thoughts and actions:

Treat other people the way you want to be treated. My mother always taught me to "Do onto others as you would have them do on to you."

Leave your home problems at home. Fellow employees hate complainers who constantly talk about their problems at work. It's also true that discussing your home issues during your work day decreases your productivity and success on your job.

Be honest and always communicate your feelings. If you don't like how you are being treated, speak up about it. Things will never change if you hold in your feelings.

Instead of picking out other people's faults, celebrate their uniqueness and differences, which is what makes life interesting. Imagine how boring it would be if we were all alike! Everyone is on a different journey and we are in different learning phases of that journey. If you have a co-worker who is not where you are at, be compassionate and know they will someday catch up to you.

Speak up and advocate for yourself. If you don't like something, say something about it.

Don't be a pushover or let people take advantage of you. This causes resentment. Create healthy boundaries.

Find something in common with your boss or coworkers that you can share.

Always come to work with a smile and try to smile throughout the day. People hate when their co-workers are grumpy cats all day. How can you expect others to be positive around you, if you are not smiling?

Always make eye contact when communicating with people.

Watch your body language. Actions speak louder than words and sometimes your body language can be imposing or threatening. There are many corporate coaches and self-improvement experts who teach courses on how to use your body language for success and also how to interpret other people's body language. If you learn this information it can give you an advantage in every relationship and situation.

Try to speak to people in a friendly tone. If you are in a bad mood, try your best to keep it under control when you talk with co-workers, employees or your boss.

Listen to the other person and be fully present. (learning Mindfulness will help)

Show people your thanks and appreciation and be polite. If you do this, others will do the same for you.

Take responsibility for your actions.

Be compassionate for other people's situations. Maybe your boss is angry because his wife cheated on him. Try to mentally step in the other person's shoes to see things from their perspective.

Offer your help to people at work whenever possible.

Be genuine, not a big phony, at work. People who are phony create a bad reputation and are disliked.

Do not pay attention to what others say behind your back. Don't take negative comments personally and do not talk about co-workers or other people behind their backs. When you talk about other people behind their back, it will come back to bite you.

Greet people when you come in to work every day and when you go out.

Do your best to be patient. Patience is a virtue and if you want others to be patient with you then you have to model the behavior.

When you make promises, always follow through on them.

Avoid people who are always mean or negative, whenever you can.

Practice forgiveness. Since holding grudges makes you sick, you need to forgive people at work when they are jerks.

Always apologize when you do something wrong.

Unfortunately, there are some people you work with who, no matter how hard you work on yourself, will never reciprocate.
Here are some tips for dealing with co-workers who are mean, annoying, abusive, argumentative, irrational, hostile and have other flaws:

Improve your listening skills because maybe their actions have to do with something you did. However you will never learn why they are behaving badly if you don't listen deeply.

When someone yells at you, argues or is hostile, first try to reason with them and if they are not able to reason, then just walk away. I give people a warning or chance to change their behavior by saying something like, "If you continue to yell at me I am going to leave, so please talk to me in a civil manner." If they continue on in nasty mode, I walk away. You can use this on the telephone too and hang up on the yelling party.

When someone is yelling or angry, ask them why they are yelling or angry. Who knows? Maybe they had a bad day, or got a divorce or they have PMS, but it's good for you to know this info so you don't take it personal and you can be more understanding of their bad behavior. If they don't have this kind of understandable source for their behavior, that is your clue that this is not a temporary occurrence but may be a regular problem with this individual.

Never argue back with people or yell at someone, because it makes you sick and they win.

Get some counseling from someone you can talk with about your co-workers.

Report an abusive co-worker to the person who is their superior. If they are a manager or supervisor who has someone they report to, you can report to their boss. However, if your boss is the only boss and doesn't have anyone to report to, you will have to reason with them, learn skills to deal with them or quit your job.

If you do everything possible to stop abuse and hostility at work and nothing changes, then it's time to consider changing jobs. Your health and life are more important than anything else and no person deserves to stay in an abusive and psychologically harmful situation. Make sure not to quit your job until you have found a new one or have enough money in the bank to do so. Remember that lack of money is the number one cause of stress!

Your Work Surroundings and Space

A comfortable work area is very important for people to be happy at a place where they spend every week of their life.

Here are some work place improvement tips:

If the temperature is uncomfortable, either do something about it, or ask someone to do something. If that is not a possibility then wear layers of clothes to work so you can take them off or put them on when needed.

Make sure you have a large enough workspace with proper lighting. If you are the boss, you can do something about this, but if you are not the boss, speak up and ask for a change. If it's not possible to change to better seating, you will have to arrange your work space as best as possible to help you work better.

Always keep your work space organized. When it's hard to find things, you will feel stressed. Spend a few minutes at the end of each day organizing your things. You can also do a big organization once a week.

Have your computer station set up ergonomically. That means your arms should always be at a 90 degree angle while typing. Your mouse needs to be close to your body and your wrists should always be straight on the keyboard. If your wrists are bent, you can get Carpal Tunnel Disorder.

If you have any vision problems, consider getting special eyeglasses just for your computer. These are prescription glasses that you wear specifically when you are on the computer. To avoid eye strain, make sure to look away from your computer out in the distance about every 20 minutes and refocus on something far away.

Keep your back and neck straight in your chair and keep your eyes looking forward at your computer. You will need to place your key board on a shelf that fits under your desk and place your computer screen up high enough, so that you are not bending your back or neck. If you scrunch up your back or neck, you will always have pain and problems. Your knees and legs should be at a 90 degree angle with your feet flat on the floor.

Turn your workplace into a peaceful oasis with these suggestions: - Add some live green plants or flowers around your workspace.

Buy a small plug-in or battery-operated water fountain. The sounds are very soothing.

Play soft and relaxing music in the background (if you work at home or in a closed office) or listen to it on headphones.

Use lavender or Roman chamomile essential oil in a diffuser near your desk. (This only works if you work alone or have co-workers who are okay with this. Please be mindful of co-workers with possible allergies to fragrance)

Buy a Himalayan Salt Crystal lamp, and plug it in next to your computer to protect you from harmful radiation. Himalayan salt releases negative ions into the air which is equivalent to sitting by a waterfall or the ocean. You can also use Sodalite or Black Tourmaline crystals by either taping them to your computer or placing them near your computer to help protect you from EMR (Electro-Magnetic Radiation).

Make sure you have a comfy chair to sit on. You can buy special cushions to put on your seat and behind your back for comfortable support.

Practice mindfulness (present moment awareness) while at work.

Job Performance and Productivity

Stress causes epic failure, decreased productivity, absenteeism and turnover at work or in a business. Stress negatively impacts your ability to make good decisions, it causes you to have accidents and injuries at work and also helps you make mistakes. Some people can cost their company a lot of money and even bankruptcy because of the effects of stress on their brain. If you are a business owner, CEO or executive who makes very important decisions every day, stress can make a huge negative impact on those decisions.

You will want to work hard to manage stress so you can improve success at work. There are many things you can do to improve productivity at work but here is my personal recipe for increasing productivity at work:

Learn and practice time management skills and have clear priorities.

Eat a healthy low sugar, high fiber, anti-inflammatory diet which helps your brain to function better and gives your body sustained energy throughout the day. If you eat 5 small meals a day or have snacks in between meals, you will have more energy. (See chapter 2 on physical stress.)

Get 8 hours of sleep every night and take little naps on days off or maybe during lunch break Meditate or exercise before work every morning 10 to 30 minutes

Practice quick breathing, visualization or meditation exercises during the day when you feel stressed, lose focus or when your productivity is dropping. You can also get up and walk around for a few minutes every few hours.

When you come home, either meditate or exercise for 10 to 30 minutes every day

Take at least 30 minutes of Me Time every day and do something fun.

Surround yourself with quality people who will support you.
Stay organized

Say "No!" to people when you have an already full schedule

Delegate tasks, projects, jobs and other chores as much as possible. Make sure that you always delegate to competent people or you will be more stressed if you have to redo the job later.

Leave your problems and worries at the door. This means you leave the work problems at work and the home problems at home. Never put the two together. Many people bring their home stresses to work with them and bring their work stresses home. This will impact your relationships, take your life out of balance and prevent you from being successful in all areas of your life and work.

Batch your outgoing emails together if possible and only check them once in the morning at 10:00 a.m. and once in the afternoon. If you check emails immediately when you get to work, you will be side-tracked from your to-do list. If you are waiting for an important message then, by all means check it more frequently.

If you work on a computer, refocus your eyes once every 20 minutes by looking at something in the distance for a few seconds. This will decrease eye fatigue and strain.

To improve your focus or concentration while working on tasks or projects, take small breaks from your work throughout the day. Get up and walk around, stand up and stretch, or close your eyes and focus on breathing for a few minutes.

Take large projects and break them down into smaller easier to accomplish tasks. It will be easier to focus on each small task, then to look at the entire whole project.

You can listen to background music like classical or jazz to keep you focused on your project and keep your mind from wandering. Classical music has been proven to improve memory, learning, intelligence, math skills, science skills, test scores and it promotes relaxation and stress relief.

Last but most important is to take regular vacations during the year and take a lunch break and/or other breaks every day. Taking breaks (even small ones) does wonders for helping productivity and also helps you to focus better when you are working. Studies have shown that people who take vacations are more productive than people who do not!

When Leaving Your Home is Stressful (Stress in Public Places)

Everywhere you go, when you leave your home, there is potential for something negative to happen. It's not a surprise to me that social phobia or social anxiety is the 3rd most common psychological problem in the United States, according to www.anxietynetwork.com. In fact, social anxiety affects at least 15 million people each year in the US alone.

Once you leave your home, some stress is out of your control, but there are plenty of things you can do to prevent unpleasant situations. When we are talking about "public place" stress, we are talking about anything negative that happens to you or that you perceive as stress when you go to the mall, grocery store, school, work, amusement park, hotel, doctor's office, park, concerts, movie theatre, airport, church, parties and other places where there are other people.

Some of the many things that people perceive as stressful include:

Going shopping. Some people love shopping but many people hate it and would prefer to never shop.

Crowds of people (especially when they are strangers). Sometimes a crowd of people whom you do know can be stressful too, like when you go to a wedding, family reunion or party.

Loud noises
Standing in lines. Whether the line is for purchasing something or to get in somewhere, it's never fun to stand in line.

Parking
Driving to a location

Being around someone you don't like (especially when it's a family member)
Cigarette smoke. If cigarette smoke bothers you, do not go to places where there will be people smoking. It's not fair to subject yourself to that.

Rude people
Poor service

Crying babies (Yes, some people don't like babies. I personally love babies and don't mind if they are crying as long as it's not on a long airplane flight.) Fear of being watched, judged or criticized by others.

Fear of being followed.
Fear of people talking to you.
And many more things that people perceive as stressful when they leave their home and go to public places.
If you are someone who knows or suspects they have a social anxiety disorder, please consider seeing a mental health counselor and getting some cognitive behavioral therapy or Hypnotherapy. It is not healthy to be afraid of leaving your home. Many years ago I had a period of a few years where I was experiencing a social anxiety disorder. Hypnotherapy combined with cognitive behavioral therapy cured me of my problem. Now I am fine in social settings.

However, if you just get normally stressed and don't have a severe case, consider these tips to help you when you go places:

To avoid crowded malls, parking and lines, shop on the Internet as much as possible. o When it's the holiday times, start your shopping earlier in the season. I start shopping in September every year and put things away in a closet until the holidays, so that I can enjoy the holidays instead of running around to crowded malls.

If you go out shopping and have to stand in lines, take a friend with you, so you can chat while you are in line. It will make time go by quickly. You can also bring a small book or just catch up on emails on your smart phone.

To avoid the parking mess, get to the stores really early to get a good spot, or park away from the shopping center and walk over to it. You will avoid the stress of hunting down a parking spot. And of course, walking is good exercise for you and also relieves stress!

If you have social anxiety, learn how to practice breathing exercises, mantras and other calming activities that you can use when you have to be in a social situation.

If going out to other people's parties makes you stressed, consider hosting your own. Sometimes, being in familiar surroundings makes it easier. You can also learn how to say "Sorry I can't come" or "I wish I could come but maybe some other time", when people invite you to parties.

If loud noises bother you in public places, try bringing ear plugs or noise cancelling headphones. These work great on airplanes, especially when there's screaming babies on 14 hour international flights. LOL

I personally use ear plugs at football games, movie theatres and other places where the noise causes hearing damage. My piano teacher always wears ear plugs during her lessons to protect her hearing.

Plan plenty of time to get to public places and also plenty of time to do what you are going for. Lack of time to travel or accomplish something will cause even greater stress than the event itself.

Driving Stress, Road Rage and the Work Commute

Transportation of all types can be stressful to most people, whether it's a bus, train, plane, care, truck, motorcycle, boat, motorhome, jet ski or golf cart. Buying, selling, owning, cleaning, maintaining and repairing a vehicle or any other type of transportation can cause a fair amount of stress. Then, if you add in long commutes to work, your stress levels will rise. People who have mental problems, short tempers, lack of compassion, anger issues, history of violence, or don't have patience are at high risk for road rage. Road rage is becoming a common problem in the United States and too many people in the United States die in car crashes or from gunshot wounds affiliated with road rage. The stress from driving can make you sick and shorten your life whether you have anger issues or not.

If you live far from your job and/or have a long commute, or you live in an area with lots of traffic, there are only a few things you can do about it:

Move closer to your work.
Take a bus or train.
Get into a carpool or vanpool.
Quit your job and get one closer to home.

If none of these are an option, you will have to learn how to manage your driving stress. You may live close to work and still hate driving. Some people are stressed every time they drive. Others are only stressed in traffic, when someone is rude and cuts them off, when someone doesn't let them in, or when there is an accident or other adverse driving situation. Also, there are times when you are driving with people who are distracting you or giving you stress. One example is kids trying to talk to you or making too much noise while you drive.

Whatever it is that causes you stress while you drive, here are some tips for managing your driving stress.

If you have young children in your car, make sure to keep them busy with books, videos, games, kids music CD's, food they can eat on their own.

Make sure to plan adequate extra time in your schedule when you have to drive to appointments to account for possible traffic jams, accidents and other things that might make you late.
Most accidents happen from distracted driving so if you want to stay out of an accident, don't smoke, eat, drink, put makeup on your face, talk or text on your cell phone while driving. Don't turn your head to talk with the person in the seat next to you. I know someone who did this and got into a bad crash. If you are talking with someone via cell phone, make sure to use a hands-free device, so you do not get a ticket or accident. Tickets and accidents cause a whole new level of stress.

Don't judge the drivers who are behaving badly on the road and swear at them. That person may be driving badly, but you don't know what they are like off the road or what their circumstance is. Maybe they are in a hurry to pick up an injured family member. Whenever you criticize, judge and yell at other drivers, you are actually harming yourself on an energetic, mental and physical level with negative thoughts, negative speech and negative energy. Just mindfully note that some guy cut you off and return to focusing on the road.

Practice the art of mindfulness and really focus 100% on the road. Don't allow your mind to go off to past or future, just think about the now.

If you are stuck in traffic, know that you have no control over the traffic. Getting angry will just cause you stress which will make you sick. Instead, just relax and listen to a book on tape, a radio talk show, the news or other thing to distract your attention from the traffic.

If you are driving with other people, you can have a nice conversation to keep your mind off traffic issues.

If you are driving alone, change your perception of driving from being negative to being a positive experience. Think of driving as time alone with your thoughts and no work. Think of your vehicle as your little fortress of solitude, where there are no bosses or family members to bother you. There is no work to do, other than focusing on the road. Use your time alone to: be creative and come up with ideas; go over your day and think about what improvements you can make; recite a speech you have to deliver; listen to great music; listen to books on CD and learn something; daydream; expand your imagination and whatever else you can come up with.

Some people reading this book may have stress from fears related to driving. Many years ago, I would have panic attacks while driving and also some fainting spells while driving, which gave me a fear of driving my car. I had to have people take me everywhere. It was one of the worst times of my life. Fortunately, I love driving my car again and don't have any more fear. I know many people who are afraid of driving and some who are only afraid of driving on freeways. I also know many people who are afraid of flying, taking busses and trains and so on. If you have a transportation phobia, consider seeing a good mental health therapist and/or hypnotherapist. The hypnotherapy worked really well for me. The other tool I used for myself and still use to this day is the mantra:

"I am safe and protected everywhere I go"

Last thoughts on Managing Environment Stress

Whether you are at home, work, public places or driving your car, you are in the driver's seat. Pardon my humor! You are in control over most of what happens in your life and you co-create everything with God. If you don't like your home, you can choose to change it or move. If you don't like driving, you can choose to take a bus. If you don't like your job, you can either change jobs or start your own business.

You are the one making the choices. Every now and then something will happen that you could not prevent, delete or control, like a water heater that breaks or a washing machine with a leak. When these things happen at work or at home, please see all of them as little speed bumps in your road of life that can be used as a learning experience. Every time something happens that you have no control over, ask God, "What can I learn from this situation?" You can also ask, "How can I use this situation to help others?" This is a great way to be of service to the planet. I turned a lifetime of learning experiences into a business where I help people to make their lives better.

Activities for Managing Environment Stress

Use the suggestions on Financial/Money stress and write up a plan or list of items for improving your relationship with money. If you are married, it's important to do this activity with your spouse. Include with your plan a monthly budget. If you don't have a financial planner, consider meeting with one to help you plan for your retirement.

Spend a day creating a relaxing oasis in your home. You can either do things to make your entire home peaceful, or you can pick one room in your house and set it up with items like candles, plants, oil diffuser, meditation cushions and some soft music.

Spend some time at work setting up your work area to be ergonomic for your body and making your work area more comfortable and relaxing.

If you are unhappy with your job and don't want to change jobs, quit or retire, make up a list of all the things at your job that you do not like or that are stressful. Then write down some action items for each thing you list so that you can make changes.

For example if you write that a certain coworker is rude to you, then your plan would say: "Have discussion with co-worker on how we can get along" or "Have conversation with boss about co-worker's behavior."

As another example, if your work area is too small, you would create a list of things you can do to expand the space or make it workable.

CHAPTER 6
TOOLS, MODALITIES AND ACTIVITIES TO MANAGE STRESS

Create Your Own Personal Stress Management Tool Kit

In this chapter I will be covering many different tips and ideas for managing overall stress. I cannot possibly cover everything there is, so feel free to use your own creativity!

After you read the long list of ideas, you will get to make your own Stress Management Tool Kit. This is something I have been giving my clients for years. Everyone I give this to, is very grateful and they give me amazing testimonials for how this tool kit has helped them.

I don't expect you to do everything on this list to manage your stress. These are just examples and guidelines. You will need to pick out the activities, tools or modalities that fit best with your personality, spiritual beliefs and lifestyle. You will want to research the ones you have not heard of before. Make sure you inform your doctor that you are using these techniques and if you have a negative reaction to any of them, please stop immediately and consult your doctor.

Tools, Modalities and Activities For Overall Relaxation and Stress Management

Give yourself permission to take time for yourself. Spend at least 30 minutes a day to an hour, relaxing and taking some down time.

Time management skills. If you don't manage your time well, take some classes or read a book on how to manage time. I have been teaching time management for many years and would love to help you. I have created an affordable audio class that will be available real soon on my website entitled, "Time for Self, Family and Fun – Easy Tools for Time Management". By the time you read this book, it may already be there. You can find out more at https://spiritualgrowthjourneys.com.

Simplify everything in your life, both at home and work. Learn ways to delegate, do less, and make projects smaller and easier to deal with. Eliminate all of the things in your life that are not necessary. For example, we had a boat that we liked but were not using much and it was costing us time and money to take care of, so we got rid of it. Make a list of all the things in your life and at work that you can simplify or get rid of and start doing them. Try a website called www.simpleology.com where you can learn hundreds of tips for simplification.

Learn how to create and maintain a healthy work life balance. Leave your problems at the door and don't bring work issues home or home issues to work. Don't work more than a 40 hour week. Learn to work smart, not hard. Read up on how to create a healthy work-life balance or get help from a coach like me.

Keep your home and office organized so you can find things easily.

Take a vacation every year. If you can take a vacation two or more times a year, that's even better! Weekend getaways are good and if you don't have money, try camping, visiting family or a stay-cation (staying at home and relaxing).

Exercise for at least 10 minutes and no more than one hour each day. Studies show that 10 minutes of interval training or aerobic exercise every day is very good for the body. Also, exercising too much causes an increase in cortisol (the primary stress hormone), so one hour is enough.

Do relaxation exercises. These can include gentle stretching, night-time yoga, chigong, progressive relaxation of your body, and visualization.

Take a vacation from your electronics. Dedicate one day a week to a vacation away from checking email, going on the computer or tied to your cell phone. Absolutely do this while away on vacations. It's not a real vacation if you are hooked to electronic devices.

Laughter is the best medicine so make yourself laugh every day with a funny video, TV show, movie, comedy club, telling jokes, acting silly and other joys.

Smile always. Smiling releases positive neurotransmitters to your brain. Laugh lines are better looking than stress wrinkles and saggy, baggy skin from stress.

Practice daily gratitude. Always remember that no matter how bad things are, there are millions of other people who are worse off than you are. Be grateful for every moment.

Use aromatherapy. Lavender oil, chamomile and jasmine, Melissa (Lemon Balm), Oil of bergamot, chocolate and vanilla fragrance are all great for stress relief.

Herbs and herbal teas. Passionflower, Melissa (Lemon Balm), St. John's Wort and Chamomile are all helpful but check with a Naturopathic doctor before using them.

Essential oils. Lavender, bergamot, cedar, Roman Chamomile, Lemon Balm and many others can be helpful for stress, depression and anxiety. Essential oils can be used by putting them into a diffuser in the room, breathing them in on a tissue or dabbing them on your skin. Be careful because many of them need to be mixed with another carrier oil before putting on your skin or they can cause irritation. Check with your doctor first before trying these.

Breathing exercises or breath-work (Pranayama breathing). When you are stressed, you either hold your breath, chest breathe, hyperventilate or shallow-breathe. Oxygen is the most important element that you need to stay healthy, so not breathing properly is harmful to your body. There is a little electronic device called a "Breath trainer" you can purchase to help you with breathing.

Humans are born doing full belly breathing. When you re-learn how to do full bellybreathing and special relaxation breathing, it helps to reduce stress and improve your health. Please research breathing methods for relaxation on the internet or take some classes. This is one of the first lessons I give my students.

Practice Mindfulness Based Stress Reduction (present moment awareness). I became certified to teach this method because it totally changed my life and I use it every day.

Spend some time in nature. Gardening, camping trips, picnics at the park, hiking, birdwatching, kayaking, boating, walking and bicycling get you out in nature. You can walk in the rain with a good umbrella.

Spend time near water – Waterfalls, streams, rivers, lakes and oceans.

Earthing. Walk barefoot on the grass or sand or sit with your back against a tree for 15 minutes. Scientific studies show that Earthing can lower blood pressure and improve your immune system and overall health.

Journaling. First thing in the morning or right before bed time is a great time to write in your journal. Put your feelings and thoughts on paper and get them out of your head.

Pet therapy. Spend time with animals, especially petting them, cuddling with them, playing with them and loving them. They will love you back unconditionally.

Meditation. There are over 108 different types of meditation, including mindfulness, transcendental, progressive relaxation, listening to music or sound, Qi Gong, Zen, Taoist, yoga and guided visualization. Also consider prayer.

Sound Therapy – Whether you are listening to soft music, binaural beats, tuning forks, chanting, drumming, singing bowls or chimes, the healing energy of sound has a profound effect on the body and has been used for thousands of years. Sound healing is the oldest, most gentle and most profound method of healing there is. Sound therapy suggests that by projecting the correct resonant frequency back into an imbalanced body part or into a stressed individual, it could possibly restore the natural harmony. Some of my favorite C.D.'s with sound healing come from James Twyman, Jonathan Goldman, Stephen Halpern and Kimba Arem. You can find C.D.'s by these amazing musical artists/healers on the internet.

Tai chi and chi gong classes

Yoga. There are several types of yoga you can try. The most common types of yoga are: Hatha, Vinyasa, Iyengar, Kundalini, Bikram and Ashtanga. Warning: Hot yoga can be harmful to your health, so I do not recommend it. When you exercise in high temperatures, it not only stresses the body, but can cause dehydration, dizziness, high blood pressure, heart palpitations, fainting and other health problems. Always do yoga classes at a comfortable and safe room temperature.

Martial arts, a great way to channel frustration and anger.

Go dancing. Dance in your home or take dancing classes. (Dance like no one is watching.)

Try different emotional healing techniques like Emotional Freedom Techniques, EMDR, Psych-K, Emotion Codes or Healing Codes, Hypnosis, Cognitive behavioral therapy and others.

Practice Spirituality. This is not the same as religion. This involves personal rituals, beliefs and practices that are individual and unique to you. Everyone expresses spirituality differently. Spirituality can be a great way to get connected directly to your creator; get to know your higher self and connect to your spirit. Get connected to everyone and everything in the universe.

See a mental health therapist and talk about your problems.

Simplify and organize your life. Try a website called www.simpleology.com.

Spend time with friends. Go out to a movie, lunch, drinks, take a girls trip or experience some other type of social fun.
Spend time with your family.

Get or give a hug every day. Human touch is important for reducing stress.

Do a craft or fun hobby (knitting, sewing, trains, painting, R.C. cars)

Hot showers, sauna, hot tub or bubble bath. Warm water or steam is relaxing.

Go to a party.

Go to an amusement park.

Listen to music, sing or play musical instruments. Go to a concert.

Fly a kite, build a sand castle or otherwise get in touch with your inner child.

Play fun board games, cards games or other pretend games with your kids or friends.

Have sex with a committed partner (use appropriate protection), or by yourself if that is your situation. Sex and orgasm releases hormones that make you feel good like serotonin and oxytocin and sex helps to balance the other hormones. A good book to read is Orgasm for Life by Jennifer Elizabeth Masters.

Eat chocolate, especially dark chocolate, which is good for your heart and releases serotonin which is a feel-good hormone.

Go get a massage, reiki, acupuncture or reflexology – all of these modalities are very good for stress relief. There are places in the United States, where you can buy a yearly massage membership and get a massage at least once a month at a discounted price.

Treat yourself to a manicure, pedicure or facial.

Go shopping. (only if you really have the money to spend)

Take a break from cooking and cleaning up every night; go out to eat at a restaurant.

Use all of the emotional healing info you learned in Chapter 2 on emotional stress.

Sit down and do absolutely nothing. Sometimes this is what you need to de-stress.

Create Your Custom Stress Management Toolbox

This is your custom go-to list of tools and techniques that you can use any time you feel stressed. You will be creating this toolbox with things that resonate with you or that you enjoy. The toolbox is organized by the amount of time that you have available, when you are feeling stressed.

You can pick some of my examples from the examples below and the list above and/or add in your own ideas depending on your interests. Make sure you are specific with the activities you want to do; instead of saying "do a hobby," you would list "knit blanket for 15 minutes."

The last section of the tool box is a blank template that you can photocopy and fill out with the activities you wish to do and that you will follow through on. When you use your list, pick different activities and mix them up every day so that you do not get bored.

Once you have a list composed, keep a few copies of it around in different spots, where you can pull it out and use it when you need to. Keep at least one at home and one at work in your locked desk drawer or purse.

Examples:

Here are some examples of what your stress management tool may look like:

I have 1 minute to 15 minutes of time (Most of these examples are 5 minute items)

Visualization with eyes closed (visualize something fun, calm or relaxing like a beach in Hawaii.)
Breathing exercise
Progressive Relaxation (Scan your body quickly. Relax and release all areas with tension)
Quick meditation, close eyes and focus on your breath or music for a few minutes.

Listen to or sing a song
Read a joke or watch funny You-Tube video
Read a short magazine article
Say some Affirmations

Say a Prayer
Get up and do some stretching
Have a glass of water with a slice of lemon (citrus is uplifting)
Breathe in the scent of some relaxing or uplifting essential oils (lavender, bergamot, citrus)

Any other things you can do in a few minutes
Pet and love on your dog or cat or spend time with a pet of your choosing

I have 20 - 30 minutes of time:

Meditation – Any style (mindfulness, visualization, zen, prayer, etc.)
Breathing exercises, more intensive
Take a walk

Other types of exercise (bicycle, jog, aerobics, weights, dance.)
Read a book, magazine or website article.
Watch a TV show, preferably comedy or something light. (Laughter is good medicine. Do not watch violence when you are stressed out. Studies show that watching violence elevates blood pressure and stress hormones.)

Call or text a friend. (Studies show that talking with a friend and socializing is great for your health.)
Take a hot shower or hot bath

Get a 30 minute seated massage
Work on a hobby, like knitting, crocheting, drawing, painting, or some other fun creative hobby that you enjoy.

I have one or more hours of time:

Meditation with breathing exercises
Exercise of your choice (aerobics, weights, bicycling.)
Play sports

Go on a hike or walk

Take a hot bath or sit in a hot tub

Have lunch with a friend

Talk with, or hang out with a friend.

Watch TV or movie that is light in tone

Listen to music or sing

Play an instrument.

Get a massage, reiki, reflexology, Mani-Pedi, acupuncture, facial or other relaxing body service.

Go shopping.

Do nothing/relax.

Do something creative.

Work on a hobby you enjoy (sewing, RC cars, building stuff, art.)

My Stress Management Tool Kit – Things I can do when I am stressed I have 1 minute to 15 minutes of time. These are some things I can do for stress:

1.

2.

3.

4.

5.

6.

7.

8.

9.

10.

I have 15 to 30 minutes of time. These are some things I can do for stress:
1.
2.
3.
4.
5.
6.
7.
8.
9.
10.

I have 30 minutes to one hour of time. These are some things I can do for stress:
1.
2.
3.
4.
5.
6.
7.
8.
9.
10.

I have one or more hours of time. These are some things I can do for stress:
1.
2.
3.

4.

5.

6.

7.

8.

9.

10.

CHAPTER 7
TOTAL LIFE MAKEOVER

A re you ready to live a longer, happier and healthier life? Are you ready to make improvements in your life?

Now that you have read this book and learned about the P.E.A.C.E. Stress Management System®, this is the chapter where you are going to pull it all together into a plan. In all of the other chapters, I listed action items to start managing stress in the 4 major categories. They were fairly simple, but now I am giving you the challenge to get your life going in the right direction.

In this chapter, you will be completing a worksheet and plan to get started changing every portion of your life that you want to change - your P.E.A.C.E. Stress Management System® total life makeover plan.

I have given you some examples for each of the items in this plan, so you have an idea of what to put on your own plan. This worksheet will be a guide to help you with the next steps you need to take to have the great life that you were created for.

If you are someone who only needs to make a few changes, instead of changing everything in your life, no worries. Go through this entire worksheet and pick the things that apply to you and the things you "want" to change. I am not here to force you to change anything! I am here to teach you how to make the changes that you want to make in your life. YOU are 100% in control of your own life and you need to be the one who makes the changes. No one is going to do this for you and no one should tell you how to live your life or what you should change.

An old friend of mine used to say, "Don't play in other people's backyards." I always respect every person's journey and I was put here on earth to help and teach the people who want my help. You are on your own journey and need to make the choices and decisions to do what is best for your highest good.

To get going with your total life makeover plan, you will need a few pencils and several sheets of paper, or you can use a computer and type the information. You can put some or all of your answers in the spaces provided in the book, but if you are like me, you will run out of space and need the paper or computer. You won't want to write in pen because you are going to probably edit it at least a few time or maybe several times. If you are someone who doesn't like to write longhand, go ahead and put your information into a Word or Google doc or an Excel spreadsheet. When I type up my own plans, I prefer the Excel spread sheet so I can put in different columns of information with numbers, dates or times.

Increasing Your Probability of Success

Before you work on your total life makeover plan here are some very important tips to help you achieve success:

Work on your plan in a quiet, private place so you can think all the information through before writing it down.

Don't have any expectations of yourself and this plan, other than that you are going to do your best to work through it. Having an expectation will just cause more stress which is counter-productive.

Go easy on yourself. When you are writing things like, "Work on my perfectionism", or "Retrain my brain to stop judging", don't be hard on yourself, judge yourself or go into a long discussion in your head about why you have this issue to work on.

You are a human and we are all here on the planet to make tons of mistakes and learn. You are not perfect. No human is perfect. Just list your ideas and start working on it.

If there are people in your life who are negative or not very supportive of you, do not share your plan with them or tell them that you are doing this work on yourself. They will only say something negative to you that will set you back in your work, create upper barrier limits or harm you on an emotional stress and energetic level. Only share your plan with people who are 100% loving and supportive of you.

This plan is not a competition or race, so don't worry about how long it will take you to implement the plans. If you are a gung ho life-fixer like I am, you will probably write it and then go crazy getting every item crossed off your list. This isn't optimal! Take however much time you need to work your plan and make changes in your life.

Major life changes usually take 6 months to a year or more, depending on what they are. If it's something like healing your adrenals, it can take one to seven years depending on how badly burned-out you are. It probably took you a lifetime to create any stress, relationship or health problems that you currently have so don't expect an overnight repair.

Look at this plan in a positive light, as a fun adventure to get to know yourself better and to get to learn and grow as a person. You are NOT broken. You don't need to fix yourself. This is all about learning some lessons and making some changes when you are ready and willing to make them.

Make sure to have a computer or Internet-capable cell phone ready when you start composing your plan because you will need to do some web searches to help you.

If you have to ask for someone's opinion while composing your plan, remember to only ask someone who wants your best and highest good and has no personal agenda and a non-biased opinion. Pick someone that has some knowledge about subjects like alternative health, stress, mental health or healing. Don't ask someone who has really strong radical beliefs (especially strong conservative religious beliefs) to assist you with this, because the outcome will be an epic failure. Don't talk to people who have already made up their mind and are not willing to research the information or educate themselves.

This plan is not written in stone and you should expect to make alterations to this plan as you improve and change your life. You will add new things and take away old things.

If you really want to improve your entire life, not just a few months or years of it, I recommend you use the concepts you learned in this book, as well as your plan, for the rest of your life. When I coach my clients, I remind them that they are learning skills that will be beneficial for them every day for the rest of their lives. The same goes with this book.

When all else fails and you feel stuck with this project or have questions, reach out to me or some other coach or stress expert to help you. You can reach me through my website https://spiritualgrowthjourneys.com with any questions, comments or to schedule a consultation or coaching/healing session.

Let's get started with your total life makeover plan now. If you run out of space on a book page, make sure to have extra paper or a computer handy. You can also make photocopies of the book pages to write on.

P.E.A.C.E. Stress Management System® – Total Life Makeover Plan

Date: _____

Daily   Improvement   Commitment:
_____hours/minutes

(How much time am I willing to dedicate each day/week/month to making these changes so I can live a longer, happier and healthier life?)

My Steps for making time in my schedule for implementing my life makeover plan: (Examples: Take a time management course, change around your priorities, put yourself on the schedule each day, improve habits, learn to say no, so you are not overloaded during the day, delegate, get someone to help, etc.)

_____

_____

_____

_____

_____

_____

_____

_____

_____

_____

_____

_____

_____

_____

_____

_____
_____
_____
_____
_____
_____

Areas I need to work on to manage physical stress? (Examples: Diet, vitamins, minerals, supplements, exercise, pain management, stop drinking or smoking, get more sleep etc.)

_____
_____
_____
_____
_____
_____
_____
_____
_____
_____
_____
_____
_____
_____
_____

Areas I need to work on to manage emotional stress? (Examples: get rid of worries, conquer my fears, stop judging, stop being a perfectionist, take more time for myself, have fun, laugh every day and etc.)

_____
_____
_____
_____
_____
_____
_____
_____
_____
_____
_____
_____
_____
_____
_____
_____

Areas I need to work on to manage chemical stress (Examples: get pesticides out of house, replace everything in house with environmentally safe cleaning products, start a body detox, put special protection devices on my cell phones and computers, put water filter in shower and etc.)

_____
_____
_____
_____

_____
_____
_____
_____
_____
_____
_____
_____
_____
_____
_____
_____
_____
_____
_____

Areas I need to work on to manage environment stress: (Examples: reduce driving stress; coping techniques for Christmas dinner with inlaws; flying on airplanes; my desk at work needs to be set up ergonomically; shopping malls.

_____
_____
_____
_____
_____
_____
_____
_____
_____
_____
_____

_____

_____

_____

_____

_____

_____

_____

_____

Action Plan for the things I wish to improve or change in my life

After you have written down a list of things you want to change under each category, take a sheet of paper and start writing a mini plan for each of the items you want to change or improve in each category. When you fill out your mini plans for each thing you want to work on, you may want to review the chapter of the book that pertains to your topic. If you have only a few things to work on in each category, you may only have a few pages in your plan. However, if you have many things you need to change in your life, you may have a large plan with many sheets of paper.

Make sure that your plan includes the people who will be supporting you through this process: your friends, family, doctors, mental health therapists and others who will support you through your life makeover plan. If you do this work all by yourself, you are setting yourself up for failure. It's important to have people to support you in your life, especially when you are trying to change or improve something. If you can't think of anyone, then you need to consider hiring a coach like me to encourage, assist and fully support you. Coaches like me teach you, mentor you and support you. Coaches are also your personal cheerleading squad, since our number one goal is your success. You will also need to include your list of resources for each subject. I have given you a blank plan page that you can photo copy as many times as you need to help you.

Here is an example of what you want on your page:

Major Stress Category: Physical Stress   Item to change: Diet

Action Plan:

Eat 5 small meals each day
Drink full glass of water between each meal
Start Weight Watchers
Find a dietician through health plan and schedule appointment
Find an acupuncturist and schedule appointment
Take herbal supplements recommended by my doctor
Weigh myself every day
Measure my body at beginning of program, so I know how well I am doing

Who Will Support me with these plan:

Name:	Phone number:	Email:
Dr. Bob Jones	(206)888-8888	bobjones@gmail.com
My sister – Susie Brown	(310)777-7777	susie@hotmail.com
My boyfriend – Gabe	(605)333-3333	gabester@yahoo.com

How much time will I dedicate to this item each day: 20 minutes

List of resources I need: (these are fictitious examples)

Books – "The Paleo Diet", "The Anti-inflammatory Diet"
CD – "Weight Loss Hypnotherapy
Websites – www.loseweightnow.com, www.moveyourbody.com, www.skinnyforever.com
Classes: weight loss class at local church, meditation class at library
Local weight loss meet up group

List of doctors, health professionals and other people who will help me:

Name of practitioner	Type	phone number	email
Dr. John McDonald	M.D.	(213)555-2222	dr.john@yahoo.com
Eva Cho Yung	Acupuncturist	(714)777-7272	acubabe@gmail.com Dorothy
Young	Dietician	(214)535-6868	Diet@dieteasy.com

Now that you have an example of how to do this plan, you are ready to make copies of the form on the next page and get busy. Remember there is no wrong or right way to do this plan. This plan is for use only and your eyes only. If you share it with someone, please only share it with someone who is non-judgmental and supports you 100%.

Major Stress Category: _____
Item to change: _____

Action Plan:

_____
_____
_____
_____
_____
_____
_____
_____
_____
_____

Who Will Support me in this plan:

Name: Phone number: Email:

_____
_____
_____
_____
_____

How much time will I dedicate to this item each day:

_____

Resources I need:
1. _____
2. _____
3. _____
4. _____

5. _____

List of doctors, health professionals and other people who will help me:

Name of practitioner	Type	phone number	email

CONCLUSION

Congratulations on completing this book! You now have a basic understanding of the 4 major types of stress that make up the P.E.A.C.E. Stress Management System®. Of course this book isn't the entire program, only an introduction to the program. However with the information you have just read, you are now on your way to living a longer, healthier and happier life.

I hope that you will use this book and its contents to create P.E.A.C.E. in every area of your life. This book's contents are a combination of spiritually-channeled information and 35 plus years of experience researching, implementing and teaching the information contained in this book. I have personally used the information in this book for many years and have improved my life, relationships, mental health and physical body.

My clients have had positive, measurable results from using the P.E.A.C.E. Stress Management System®. I hope the information in this book has been helpful for you and that you have new ideas that you can implement.

If you have enjoyed this book and you want to share any positive results you receive from using the recommendations or information in this book, please contact me through my website https://spiritualgrowthjourneys.com to share your testimonials, stories and comments.

To contact me for a private counseling session and find out more about all the many services and classes I offer, please check out my website https://spiritualgrowthjourneys.com

My fondest wish for this book is that it helps many people all over the world to have happier and healthier lives. May you and every person who reads this book, be blessed with health and happiness always.

APPENDIX A: RESOURCES

Chapter one

"Biology of Belief" – Bruce H. Lipton, PhD – Hay House books

https://www.apa.org/news/press/releases/stress/2011/final-2011.pdf

http://www.cejkasearch.com/news/press-releases/physician-stress-and-burnout- studyreveals-nearly-87-percent-of-physicians-are-moderately-to-severely-stressed/

Business News Daily – Employees Reveal How Stress Effects Their Jobs http://www.businessnewsdaily.com/2267-workplace-stress-health-epidemic-perventableemployee-assistance-programs.html

Blog - 5 Ways Your Cells Deal With Stress http://www.livescience.com/20355-5-ways-cells-dealstress.html What is a telomere? http://www.yourgenome.org/facts/what-is-a-telomere http://www.webmd.com/beauty/skin/effects-of-stress-on-your-skin

These Photos Show The Physical Toll Of Being President Of The United States http://www.huffingtonpost.com/2014/09/05/presidents-before-andafterphotos_n_5617891.html Feeling Stressed? How Your Skin, Hair And Nails Can Show It (November 12, 2007) Source:American

Academy of Dermatology
http://www.sciencedaily.com/releases/2007/11/071109194053.htm

This is your brain on stress - and it isn't pretty
http://www.naturalnews.com/049623_chronic_stress_brain_structure_mental_health.html

How to Prevent Stress From Shrinking Your Brain:
https://www.psychologytoday.com/blog/themindful-self-express/201208/howpreventstress-shrinking-your-brain

Meditation Shown to Alter Gray Matter in the Brain.
http://psychcentral.com/news/2015/01/24/meditation-shown-to-alter-graymatterinbrain/80342.html

American Psychological Association Survey Shows Money Stress Weighing on Americans' Health Nationwide
http://apa.org/news/press/releases/2015/02/money-stress.aspx
Earthing:
Health Implications of Reconnecting the Human Body to the Earth's Surface Electrons
http://www.ncbi.nlm.nih.gov/pmc/articles/PMC3265077/

Chapter 2 Resources:

http://www.truthinlabeling.org/hiddensources.html

General and Systematic Pathology - By James C. E. Underwood, MD, FRCPath, FRCP,
FMedSci and Simon S. Cross, MD, FRCPath

872 Pages, Imprint: Churchill Livingstone ISBN: 978-0-443-06888-1
Next Edition ISBN:
978-0-7020-4672-8, Copyright: 2009

http://articles.mercola.com/sites/articles/archive/2013/02/27/us-food-products.aspx

http://www.drsinatra.com http://life.gaiam.com/article/10-worst-food-additives-where-they-lurk

https://www.bodytalksystem.com/

http://classicalstretch.com/

http://www.latimes.com/science/sciencenow/la-sci-sn-sitting-health-20150119-story.html

http://well.blogs.nytimes.com/2015/04/15/the-right-dose-of-exercise-for-a-longer-life/?_r=0 http://wellnessmama.com

Chapter 3 Resources:

http://www.brianlukeseaward.com/downloads/SuperStress-WELCOA-Seaward.pdf

http://www.livescience.com/7059-keys-happiness.html

http://www.huna.com/process-of-hooponopono/

http://www.huffingtonpost.com/ocean-robbins/having-gratitude-_b_1073105.html

http://www.unstuck.com/gratitude.html

http://www.health.com/health/gallery/0,,20646990_2,00.html

http://www.webmd.com/anxiety-panic/guide/mental-health-anxiety-disorders
https://www.psychologytoday.com/blog/brainsnacks/201203/the-only-5-fears-we-all-share

https://www.brucelipton.com/resource/article/epigenetics

http://www.nih.gov/researchmatters/september2010/09272010stress.htm

http://www.liferesearchacademy.com/regression/history-of-plr.html

https://www.psychologytoday.com/blog/spiritual-wisdom-secular-times/201103/whatisspirituality

http://nccc.georgetown.edu/body_mind_spirit/definitions_spirituality_religion.html Chapter 4 Resources:

http://www.cnn.com/2014/03/27/health/cdc-autism/

http://www.honeycolony.com/article/10-things-every-american-know-toxins-in-the-body/

http://www.nytimes.com/2013/04/14/sunday-review/think-those-chemicals-have- beentested.html?_r=0

http://responsibletechnology.org/10-reasons-to-avoid-gmos/

http://foodmatters.tv/articles-1/top-10-food-additives-to-avoid
http://preventdisease.com/news/13/030313_20-Ingredients-To-Memorize-and-Avoid-InANYFoodYou-Consume.shtml
http://articles.mercola.com/sites/articles/archive/2013/04/30/waterfluoridation-facts.aspx

http://fluoridealert.org/

http://www.usgs.gov/themes/factsheet/146-00/

http://www.seafoodwatch.org/-/m/sfw/pdf/guides/mba-seafoodwatch- nationalguide.pdf?la=en

http://www.pbs.org/newshour/rundown/the-real-story-behind-the-worlds-first-antibiotic/

http://www.thehealthyhomeeconomist.com/how-to-use-best-natural-antibiotics/

http://www.brendawatson.com/road-to-perfect-health/
http://weightmaven.org/2010/12/05/brenda-watson-the-gut-probiotics/

http://www.marksdailyapple.com/prebiotics/#axzz3ox1pzYrR

http://www.drperlmutter.com/eat/brain-maker-foods/

http://bodyecology.com/articles/prebiotics_essential_to_heart_health.php

http://www.forbes.com/sites/melaniehaiken/2012/03/12/dangerous-beauty-top5contaminated-
beauty-products/

http://www.safecosmetics.org/get-the-facts/chemicals-of-concern/
http://www.totalhealthmagazine.com/Allergies-Asthma/Consumers-Beware-ToxinsLurkinginYour-Clothing.html

http://www.globalhealingcenter.com/natural-health/11-natural-methods-for-detoxing-yourbody/

Chapter 5 Resources

http://anxietynetwork.com/content/what-social-anxiety-is-like

ABOUT THE AUTHOR

Kimberly Palm is an Author, Spiritual Teacher, counselor, adviser and healer. She lives in the Pacific Northwest of the United States with her family. She combines many years of research, teaching, consulting, counseling and speaking experience with her intuitive and empathic gifts to help people have better lives and assist them on their spiritual journey. Kimberly is trained and certified in many modalities of Energy Healing and is a Certified Meditation and Mindfulness Instructor. Kimberly is also the author of the best-selling book "Ascension 101: A Roadmap for Your Soul".

Kimberly has studied metaphysics. Spirituality, esoterics, world religion, energy healing, holistic health, stress management and alternative medicine for most of her life. Kimberly offers private sessions for clients and teaches workshops and classes too.

To learn more about Kimberly and her programs, to book a spiritual counseling session, collaborate on a project or interview or hire Kimberly to speak/teach at your event go to https://spiritualgrowthjourneys.com

Made in the USA
Columbia, SC
23 February 2024

31946792R00174